Notes on

NONLINEAR SYSTEMS

Notes on

NONLINEAR SYSTEMS

by

J. K. AGGARWAL
University of Texas
Austin

VNR
VAN NOSTRAND REINHOLD COMPANY
NEW YORK CINCINNATI TORONTO LONDON MELBOURNE

Van Nostrand Reinhold Company Regional Offices:
New York Cincinnati Chicago Millbrae Dallas

Van Nostrand Reinhold Company International Offices:
London Toronto Melbourne

Library of Congress Catalog Card Number: 76-185872

Manufactured in the United States of America

Published by Van Nostrand Reinhold Company
450 West 33rd Street, New York, N.Y. 10001

Published simultaneously in Canada by Van Nostrand Reinhold Ltd.

15 14 13 12 11 10 9 8 7 6 5 4 3 2 1

PREFACE

These *Notes* were conceived and written in conjunction with a one-semester course taught at The University of Texas at Austin. Their purpose is to provide an introduction to nonlinear systems to students drawn from several engineering departments, including Electrical Engineering. The text presents qualitative, quantitative and digital computer methods for the analysis of nonlinear systems. The fundamentals of nonlinear analysis, namely the concepts of stability and oscillation, are presented for the reader in a simple but rigorous manner. A novel feature of the text is the unified and interrelated presentation of these concepts. Emphasis is placed on motivating the reader, and on developing and illustrating the methods of analysis. Examples are drawn from a variety of disciplines to illustrate the principles and show the wide applicability of the concepts and techniques studied. Exercises are provided to give the reader a better grasp of the subject through the application of techniques presented. An extensive bibliography is given to assist the interested reader in the investigation of more advanced topics.

The reader is introduced to nonlinear systems via second-order differential systems and the qualitative analysis of such systems in the phase plane. The phase-plane analysis is followed by the concepts of equilibrium point and stability in a more general setting. Various types of stability are then discussed, and several different methods for the determination of system stability are considered, including those of Liapunov and Popov. The existence of periodic solutions to nonlinear systems is considered next. Emphasis is given to limit cycles, amplitude bounds for periodic solutions, and Liapunov-like methods for the evaluation of amplitude bounds. The study of oscillatory behavior is continued with quasilinear systems and relaxation oscillations. Techniques for the approximation of solutions are presented. A discussion of digital computer methods for the solution of nonlinear differential systems follows. Included in this discussion are Picard's Iterates, Numerical Integration Methods, and Runge-Kutta type methods. Numerical solutions are presented to illustrate the techniques.

The prerequisites are minimal: an elementary knowledge of matrix algebra and the theory of differential equations is sufficient to pursue the material presented. There is a section of mathematical background to familiarize the reader with the more-often-used mathematical tools. The book may, therefore, be used as a text for a one-semester course at the first-year graduate level or senior-year undergraduate level. The material has been tried at both levels at The University of Texas at Austin. The present text complements the books of Polak and Wong and of Desoer on Linear System Theory in the present series of *Notes on System Sciences*.

The references are listed alphabetically. The number in square brackets following a name gives the number of the reference in the list for that particular author. In the transliteration of Russian names, the spelling most common in English literature is used in the text. However, in citing a reference, the spelling as it appears in the reference is used. A list of alternate spellings is given at the beginning of the reference list to facilitate the use of the bibliography.

It is a pleasure to acknowledge the encouragement,

suggestions, and discussions of many of my colleagues. In particular, I would like to thank Professors C. A. Desoer, A. R. Bergen and R. A. Skoog at the University of California, Berkeley, Professors L. G. Clark and W. C. Duesterhoeft and Dr. E. P. F. Kan at The University of Texas at Austin, and Professor C. L. Coates of the University of Illinois, Urbana. I am grateful to many students, particularly R. Richter and T. Lewis, for their contributions through perceptive questions and interesting discussions. Professor G. L. Turin, the editor of this series, was extremely helpful through his editorial and technical comments.

The manuscript was typed by Mrs. M. Thomas and Miss N. Bagley through its many versions, and the final camera copy was produced by Mrs. B. Vrtiak. It is a pleasure to acknowledge the help of these ladies.

J. K. AGGARWAL

Austin, Texas
September 1971

CONTENTS

CHAPTER I

INTRODUCTION

1. *Examples of Nonlinear Systems*

The study of a given physical system begins with the construction of a mathematical model. The mathematical model which "best" describes a given physical system depends upon physical factors as well as the objectives of mathematical modelling. The physical factors include ranges of variables, assumptions on various components of the system, and the coupling of these components. The objectives of the modelling will influence the choice of the mathematical technique, qualitative, analytical or computational, and thus the choice of model. The desirability of a given mathematical model is judged by the closeness with which it follows and predicts the behavior of the physical system. Modelling is a difficult problem and requires insight into the physical problem before a "good" mathematical model may be constructed. These *Notes* are a study of mathematical models of physical systems which are described by nonlinear ordinary differential equations. The manner in which nonlinear problems arise and how they differ from linear problems will be illustrated by considering models of physical systems.

The elementary model of the motion of a simple pendulum, shown in Figure I-1, is described by the second order differential equation

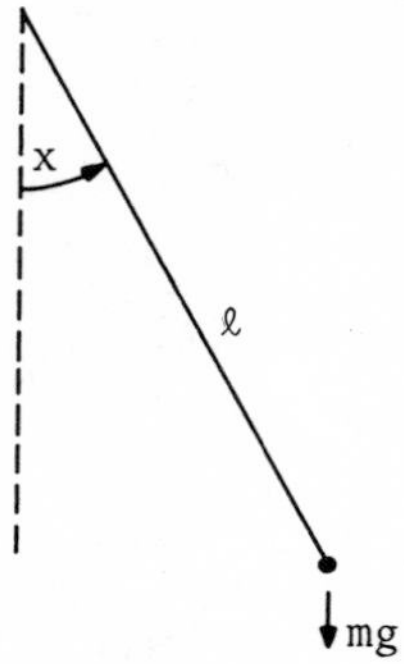

FIGURE I-1: Simple pendulum.

$$\ddot{x} + (g/\ell) \sin x = 0 \quad , \tag{1}$$

where ℓ is the length of the pendulum and g is the acceleration due to gravity. If one approximates sin x by x, for small x, the differential equation reduces to the familiar equation

$$\ddot{x} + \omega^2 x = 0 \quad , \tag{2}$$

where $\omega^2 \triangleq g/\ell$. Equation (2) describes simple harmonic motion and it arises in several situations. The differential equation (2) has for its solution

$$x(t) = A \sin (\omega t + \phi) \quad , \tag{3}$$

where A and ϕ are constants to be determined by initial conditions. The differential equation describing simple harmonic motion is an example of a linear differential equation. A linear differential equation possesses the basic superposition property, *i.e.*, if $x_1(\cdot)$ and $x_2(\cdot)$ are solutions to the differential equation, then $ax_1(\cdot) + bx_2(\cdot)$ is also a solution to the differential equation, where a and b are arbitrary constants.

An example of a nonlinear equation is the equation (1), which does not satisfy the superposition property. The differential equation (2) approximates the behavior of the pendulum for small x. For example, the period of oscillation of the model of the pendulum given by (1) depends upon the initial conditions, whereas the period of oscillation for simple harmonic motion is independent of initial conditions. Here the choice of the model depends significantly upon the range of the variables.

The block diagram of Figure I-2 models a control system which contains a plant and an amplifier. The system is described by the *nth*-order differential equation

$$\dot{x} = Ax - b\phi(\sigma)$$
$$\sigma = c'x \quad ,$$

where A is an n×n matrix, b and c are n-vectors. The transfer function of the plant is given by $G(s) = c'(sI-A)^{-1}b$ and $\phi(\cdot)$ describes the characteristics of the amplifier. If

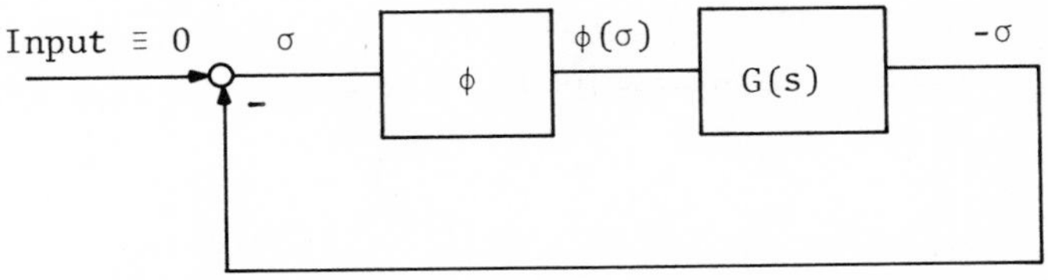

FIGURE I-2: Control system.

$\phi(\sigma)$ is a linear function of σ, *i.e.*, if $\phi(\sigma) = h\sigma$, where h is a positive constant, a simple calculation shows that the property of superposition holds. In certain engineering applications it is not possible to specify the exact nature of $\phi(\cdot)$; moreover, the function $\phi(\cdot)$ may change due to aging of the components or other effects. It is found that, in general, it is not possible to deduce the properties of a system of the above form, where the nonlinear characteristic is specified by the inequality

$$k_1\sigma \leq \phi(\sigma) \leq k_2\sigma \quad ,$$

from the consideration of linear systems of the same form but satisfying the condition $\phi(\sigma) = h\sigma$, $k_1 \leq h \leq k_2$.

A classical example of a nonlinear differential equation is van der Pol's equation

$$\ddot{x} + \varepsilon(x^2 - 1)\dot{x} + \omega^2 x = 0 \quad . \tag{4}$$

This differential equation arises in several physical situations, and one of them is shown in Figure I-3. The voltage-current relationship for the resistor is given by

$$v = x^3/3 - x \quad .$$

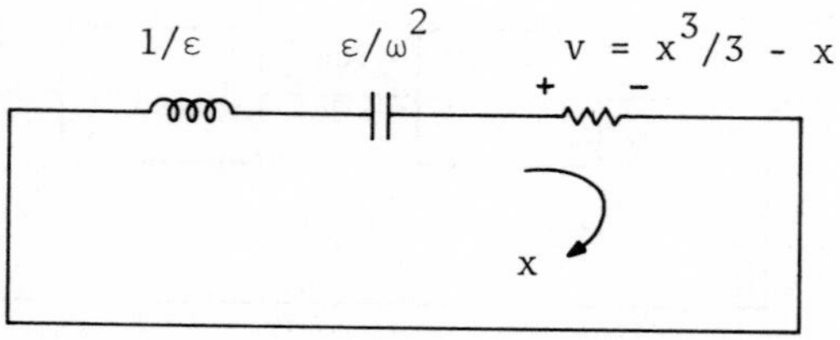

FIGURE I-3: Electrical circuit.

It may be observed that superposition does not hold for van der Pol's equation. This circuit exhibits the existence of a certain periodic solution called a "limit cycle." Limit cycles do not occur in linear systems.

In general, problems arising in physical situations are nonlinear, and the linearizations so often used are approximations, such as the approximation of sin x by x, for small x, in the case of the pendulum of Figure I-1. For many cases, linear differential equations will suffice to describe the phenomenon adequately. However, there is a large number of cases where linear treatment is not sufficient, as in the case of the control system of the Figure I-2. Further, it happens frequently that new phenomena occur in nonlinear problems which cannot occur in linear problems, as in the case of the nonlinear circuit of Figure I-3. In such cases, it is not possible to describe the phenomenon mathematically by a linear differential equation, and one must face up to the situation arising out of the essentially nonlinear character of the phenomenon.

2. *Definition of a Nonlinear System*

In the discussion above, three examples of nonlinear models have been presented, and the property of superposition of solutions has been used as a distinguishing feature. Nonlinear systems are defined via the concept of "linearity." Systems possessing the property of linearity are termed linear, and the systems lacking this property are called nonlinear. The concept of linearity in its fullest generality is a complex one, and to present a complete development of the concept would occupy an inordinate amount of space and time; however, we shall give a precise definition of linearity sufficient for our purposes.

Consider a system characterized by

$$\dot{x} = X(x(t),\ u(t),\ t) \quad , \tag{5}$$

where x is an n vector, the function $X(\cdot,\cdot,\cdot)$ is jointly continuous in all its arguments, and the partial derivatives $\partial X_j/\partial x_i$, $i,j = 1,\ldots,n$, are continuous. (X_i and x_i are, respectively, the *ith* components of X and x.) Here u(t) is the input vector to the system and x(t) is the "state" of the system. It is assumed that $u(\cdot)$ is a known continuous function. The continuity conditions are sufficient (and certainly not necessary) for the existence of a unique solution over the interval $[t_o, t_o+\varepsilon]$ for some ε, for a given initial condition $x(t_o) = x_o$, and a given continuous input function $u(\cdot)$. Existence and uniqueness of solutions will be discussed in Chapter VI.

Let $x(t,x_o,t_o,u)$ denote the solution to the differential equation (5) with initial condition x_o at $t = t_o$ and input $u(t)$, $t \geq t_o$. Then the system described by (5) is linear provided it satisfies the following three basic properties:

(i) Zero-state linearity

$$x(t,\theta_x,t_o,au_1+bu_2) \equiv ax(t,\theta_x,t_o,u_1) + bx(t,\theta_x,t_o,u_2) \ ,$$

where θ_x denotes the zero state of the system, for all inputs u_1 and u_2, constants a and b;

(ii) Zero-input linearity

$$x(t,ax_o^1+bx_o^2,t_o,\theta_u) \equiv ax(t,x_o^1,t_o,\theta_u) + bx(t,x_o^2,t_o,\theta_u) \ ,$$

where θ_u denotes the zero-input function, for all states x_o^1 and x_o^2 and constants a and b;

(iii) Decomposition property

$$x(t,x_o,t_o,u) = x(t,\theta_x,t_o,u) + x(t,x_o,t_o,\theta_u) \quad ,$$

for all states x_o and inputs u.

A discussion of the concept of linearity is found in Zadeh and Desoer [1] and Desoer [1]. It may be observed that a system described by the differential equation

$$\dot{x} = A(t)\, x(t) + B(t)\, u(t) \quad , \tag{6}$$

where $A(\cdot)$, $B(\cdot)$ are continuous matrix-valued functions of time, u is the input vector, x is the vector corresponding to the "state" of the system, is a linear system. The systems of the form (6) constitute a large class among the linear systems; however, not all linear systems can be expressed in this form. In the context of the differential systems to be studied in the following, a differential system represented by (6) may be classified as linear and a system not represented by (6) may be classified as nonlinear. This classification is not precise in terms of the general definition given earlier but it will be sufficient for our purposes in these *Notes*.

3. Methods of Analysis

The two basic notions in the analysis of nonlinear systems are stability and oscillation. The notion of stability is associated with equilibrium points of the system or the solution trajectories of the system. The interest centers around perturbations, small or large, that may disturb the system at an equilibrium point, or alter the trajectory of the system, and the behavior of the system under such a perturbation. The notion of oscillation in nonlinear systems arises from that of oscillatory motion, which may be periodic or aperiodic, forced or unforced. The properties of oscillatory motion, such as the conditions for the existence of periodic motion, the amplitude bounds, and the period of the oscillation, are of interest for the analysis of the system.

There is a wide variety of methods for dealing with nonlinear problems. However, the methods of nonlinear analysis may be broadly divided into three types:

(i) Qualitative methods,
(ii) Quantitative methods,
(iii) Computer methods.

The qualitative methods consist of finding properties of the solutions without actually finding the solution. The quantitative methods are concerned with explicitly finding closed forms of approximate or exact solutions for the nonlinear systems. The computer methods are centered around developing digital as well as analog techniques for the solutions of differential equations on digital, analog or hybrid computers.

In the present *Notes* all three types of methods will be discussed, and emphasis will be placed on developing and illustrating the basic principles of nonlinear analysis. A large number of examples will be used to illustrate these techniques. The examples will be drawn from a variety of disciplines to show the generality of the applicability of the developed techniques. In the case of computer methods, we shall restrict our attention to digital computer methods because of the easy availability of the digital computers, the ease of simulating nonlinearities on digital computers, and the ready availability of digital computer programs for the solution of differential equations.

CHAPTER II

PHASE-PLANE ANALYSIS

1. *Introduction*

We shall begin the study of nonlinear systems by considering systems described by a pair of coupled first-order differential equations:

$$\begin{aligned} \dot{x}_1 &= X_1(x_1,x_2) \\ \dot{x}_2 &= X_2(x_1,x_2) \quad . \end{aligned} \tag{1}$$

The methods of this chapter are specifically for second-order systems. The same techniques when applied to higher-order systems yield cumbersome results. The trajectory of a second-order system may be plotted in a plane and this makes the following results useful as well as making the study of second-order systems an excellent introduction to nonlinear problems.

Systems of the form (1) arise in diverse applications. For example, Volterra [1] models the growth of two competing populations by the differential equations:

$$\begin{aligned} \dot{x}_1 &= k_1x_1 - k_3x_1x_2 \\ \dot{x}_2 &= k_2x_2 - k_4x_1x_2 \quad , \end{aligned} \tag{2}$$

where x_1 and x_2 are the number of species of the two populations, respectively, and k_i, $i = 1,2,3,4$, are constants of the system. The relationship between the current i and flux

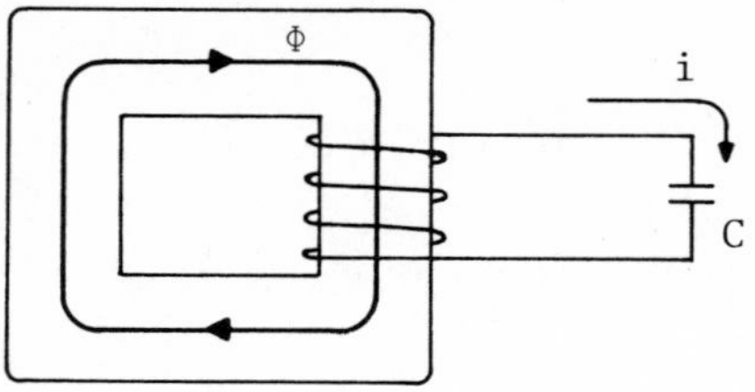

FIGURE II-1: An iron-choke circuit.

Φ for the iron choke shown in Figure II-1 is given by

$$\dot{\Phi} + \frac{1}{C}\int_0^t i(\tau)d\tau = 0 \quad . \tag{3}$$

Assuming the relationship between the current and the flux to be approximated by

$$i = A\Phi + B\Phi^3 \quad , \tag{4}$$

the system is described by

$$\begin{aligned} \dot{x}_1 &= x_2 \\ \dot{x}_2 &= -\omega^2 x_1 - \varepsilon x_1^3 \quad , \end{aligned} \tag{5}$$

where

$$\begin{aligned} x_1 &= \Phi \quad , \\ x_2 &= \dot{\Phi} \quad , \\ \omega^2 &= A/C \; , \\ \varepsilon &= B/C \quad . \end{aligned} \tag{6}$$

Still another interesting example of a second-order system

is provided by Rapoport's [1] model for the arms race between two nations. Such a race may be described by

$$\dot{x}_1 = -m_1x_1 + a_{12}x_2 + b_{12}x_2^2$$
$$\dot{x}_2 = -m_2x_2 + a_{21}x_1 + b_{21}x_1^2 \quad , \tag{7}$$

where x_1 and x_2 represent the expenditures of money by the two nations and m's, a's and b's are constants of the system.

The solutions to system (1) are studied in the (x_1,x_2)-plane and this plane is called the phase plane. Let $(x_1(t,x_{1o},x_{2o}),\ x_2(t,x_{1o},x_{2o}))$ be the solution to (1) where (x_{1o},x_{2o}) is the initial condition at $t = 0$. This solution is described in the phase plane by plotting a curve Γ with t as a parameter, and the curve Γ is called a "trajectory." A point $(\hat{x}_1,\hat{x}_2)$ in the phase plane is called a singular point for the system (1) if

$$X_1(\hat{x}_1,\hat{x}_2) = 0$$
$$X_2(\hat{x}_1,\hat{x}_2) = 0 \quad . \tag{8}$$

It is assumed that the singular points of the system are "isolated" singular points. By the term "isolated," it is meant that there is a neighborhood of the point $(\hat{x}_1,\hat{x}_2)$ in the phase plane such that this neighborhood contains no other singular point.

The assumption of continuity of the functions $X_i(x_1,x_2)$, $\dfrac{\partial X_i(x_1,x_2)}{\partial x_j}$, i, j = 1,2, enables one to expand the functions $X_1(x_1,x_2)$ and $X_2(x_1,x_2)$ in Taylor series in the neighborhood of the singular point as follows:

$$X_1(x_1,x_2)=X_1(\hat{x}_1,\hat{x}_2) + \left.\frac{\partial X_1}{\partial x_1}\right|_{\substack{x_1=\hat{x}_1\\x_2=\hat{x}_2}}(x_1-\hat{x}_1) + \left.\frac{\partial X_1}{\partial x_2}\right|_{\substack{x_1=\hat{x}_1\\x_2=\hat{x}_2}}(x_2-\hat{x}_2)$$

$$+ X_1^*(x_1,x_2,\hat{x}_1,\hat{x}_2)$$

$$X_2(x_1,x_2)=X_2(\hat{x}_1,\hat{x}_2) + \left.\frac{\partial X_2}{\partial x_1}\right|_{\substack{x_1=\hat{x}_1\\x_2=\hat{x}_2}}(x_1-\hat{x}_1) + \left.\frac{\partial X_2}{\partial x_2}\right|_{\substack{x_1=\hat{x}_1\\x_2=\hat{x}_2}}(x_2-\hat{x}_2) \tag{9}$$

$$+ X_2^*(x_1,x_2,\hat{x}_1,\hat{x}_2)$$

where

$$X_1^*(x_1,x_2,\hat{x}_1,\hat{x}_2) = o\left(\sqrt{(x_1-\hat{x}_1)^2 + (x_2-\hat{x}_2)^2}\right)$$

$$X_2^*(x_1,x_2,\hat{x}_1,\hat{x}_2) = o\left(\sqrt{(x_1-\hat{x}_1)^2 + (x_2-\hat{x}_2)^2}\right) . \tag{10}$$

The symbols o and O are explained in Appendix A. Using the notation

$$y_1 = x_1-\hat{x}_1 \quad , \quad y_2 = x_2-\hat{x}_2 \quad , \tag{11}$$

$$\left.\frac{\partial X_1}{\partial x_1}\right|_{\substack{x_1=\hat{x}_1\\x_2=\hat{x}_2}} = a_{11} \quad , \quad \left.\frac{\partial X_1}{\partial x_2}\right|_{\substack{x_1=\hat{x}_1\\x_2=\hat{x}_2}} = a_{12} \quad ,$$

$$\left.\frac{\partial X_2}{\partial x_1}\right|_{\substack{x_1=\hat{x}_1\\x_2=\hat{x}_2}} = a_{21} \quad , \quad \left.\frac{\partial X_2}{\partial x_2}\right|_{\substack{x_1=\hat{x}_1\\x_2=\hat{x}_2}} = a_{22} \quad , \tag{12}$$

$$X_1^*(x_1,x_2,\hat{x}_1,\hat{x}_2) = Y_1^*(y_1,y_2) = o\left(\sqrt{y_1^2 + y_2^2}\right)$$

$$X_2^*(x_1,x_2,\hat{x}_1,\hat{x}_2) = Y_2^*(y_1,y_2) = o\left(\sqrt{y_1^2 + y_2^2}\right) , \qquad (13)$$

the system reduces to

$$\dot{y}_1 = Y_1(y_1,y_2)$$

$$\dot{y}_2 = Y_2(y_1,y_2) , \qquad (14)$$

where

$$Y_1(y_1,y_2) = a_{11}\, y_1 + a_{12}\, y_2 + o\left(\sqrt{y_1^2 + y_2^2}\right)$$

$$Y_2(y_1,y_2) = a_{21}\, y_1 + a_{22}\, y_2 + o\left(\sqrt{y_1^2 + y_2^2}\right) . \qquad (15)$$

The process above has linearized the equations about the singular point and transferred the singular point to the origin, for $Y_1(0,0) = 0$, $Y_2(0,0) = 0$.

Definition: The singular point at the origin for the system (14) is stable if for every $\varepsilon > 0$, there exists a $\delta(\varepsilon)$ such that if

$$\sqrt{y_{1o}^2 + y_{2o}^2} < \delta ,$$

then the solution $(y_1(t,y_{1o},y_{2o}),\ y_2(t,y_{1o},y_{2o}))$ starting from (y_{1o},y_{2o}) at $t = 0$ satisfies the inequality

$$\sqrt{y_1^2(t,y_{1o},y_{2o}) + y_2^2(t,y_{1o},y_{2o})} \leq \varepsilon ,$$

for all $t \geq 0$. The singular point is unstable if it is not stable.

Neglecting terms of higher order than linear in the

equation for system (14), one can construct

$$\dot{z}_1 = a_{11} z_1 + a_{12} z_2$$
$$\dot{z}_2 = a_{21} z_1 + a_{22} z_2 \quad . \tag{16}$$

It may be observed that (16) describes a linear system whereas the system (14) is a nonlinear system. It will be assumed that $a_{11}a_{22} - a_{12}a_{21} \neq 0$, *i.e.*, the Jacobian

$$\left. \frac{\partial (X_1(x_1,x_2), X_2(x_1,x_2))}{\partial (x_1,x_2)} \right|_{\substack{x_1=\hat{x}_1 \\ x_2=\hat{x}_2}} = \left. \frac{\partial (Y_1(y_1,y_2), Y_2(y_1,y_2))}{\partial (y_1,y_2)} \right|_{\substack{y_1=0 \\ y_2=0}} \tag{17}$$

is nonsingular. A singularity which satisfies this condition is called a simple singularity. A simple singularity is an isolated singularity. The overall objective of phase-plane analysis is to determine the qualitative behavior of the system, as opposed to quantitative behavior. The qualitative behavior is exhibited by drawing trajectories in the phase plane, and such a plot is called a phase-plane plot.

Under certain circumstances it is possible to deduce the qualitative behavior of the nonlinear system from the behavior of the linear system. It is with this point of view we shall discuss second-order linear systems and derive the conditions under which a given behavior carries over to the corresponding nonlinear system.

Exercise 1: Show that a sufficient condition for the existence of the expansion (9) is that the partial derivatives $\frac{\partial X_1}{\partial x_1}$, $\frac{\partial X_1}{\partial x_2}$, $\frac{\partial X_2}{\partial x_1}$, $\frac{\partial X_2}{\partial x_2}$ be continuous in the neighborhood of the singular point $(\hat{x}_1, \hat{x}_2)$.

2. *Linear Second-Order Systems*

The linear second-order system (16) may be written as

$$\dot{z} = Az \quad , \tag{18}$$

in matrix notation, where A is a 2×2 matrix, and det A ≠ 0. The solution to the system (18) is given by (see Appendix B)

$$z(t) = \exp(At)\, z_0 \quad , \tag{19}$$

where z_0 is the initial condition at time t = 0. However, the qualitative behavior of the system (18) may be deduced from the eigenvalues of the matrix A. Consider the transformation T,

$$w = Tz \quad , \tag{20}$$

where T is a nonsingular 2×2 matrix. The differential equation for w is given by

$$\dot{w} = TAT^{-1}w \quad . \tag{21}$$

It is known that by a suitable choice of T, TAT^{-1} may be reduced to one of three canonical forms. (See Appendix B.) The canonical forms and the corresponding solutions to system (21) are as follows:

(a) *Diagonal Form* $\begin{bmatrix} \lambda_1 & 0 \\ 0 & \lambda_2 \end{bmatrix}$

Solution: $w_1(t) = w_{10}\, e^{\lambda_1 t}$, $w_2(t) = w_{20}\, e^{\lambda_2 t}$.

Eigenvalues: λ_1, λ_2;

(b) *Jordan Form* $\begin{bmatrix} \mu & 1 \\ 0 & \mu \end{bmatrix}$

Solution: $w_2(t) = w_{2o}\, e^{\mu t}$, $w_1(t) = w_{2o} t\, e^{\mu t} + w_{1o}\, e^{\mu t}$.

Repeated Eigenvalue: μ ;

(c) *Complex-Conjugate Form* $\begin{bmatrix} \alpha & -\beta \\ \beta & \alpha \end{bmatrix}$

Solution: $w_1(t) = e^{\alpha t}\,(w_{1o} \cos \beta t - w_{2o} \sin \beta t)$

$w_2(t) = e^{\alpha t}\,(w_{2o} \cos \beta t + w_{1o} \sin \beta t)$.

Eigenvalues: $\alpha+j\beta$ and $\alpha-j\beta$;

where $\lambda_1, \lambda_2, \mu, \alpha, \beta$ are real numbers, w_{1o} and w_{2o} are initial conditions.

Example: Consider the system

$$\dot{z}_1 = z_2$$

$$\dot{z}_2 = 3\alpha^2 z_1 - 2\alpha z_2 \quad ,$$

where α is a real constant. The eigenvalues of the system are α and -3α. The corresponding eigenvectors are $[{1 \atop \alpha}]$ and $[{1 \atop -3\alpha}]$. The transformation

$$w = \begin{bmatrix} 3/4 & 1/4\alpha \\ 1/4 & -1/4\alpha \end{bmatrix} z \quad ,$$

gives the system

$$\dot{w} = \begin{bmatrix} \alpha & 0 \\ 0 & -3\alpha \end{bmatrix} w \quad .$$

This transformation matrix is the inverse of the matrix

$$\begin{bmatrix} 1 & 1 \\ \alpha & -3\alpha \end{bmatrix} ,$$

the matrix obtained by adjoining eigenvectors.

Various configurations of trajectories arise depending upon the sign and magnitude of the eigenvalues of the matrix A. These configurations are discussed next.

Node: Let λ_1 and λ_2 both be negative. The point $(w_1(t), w_2(t))$ tends to the origin as $t \to \infty$ and the trajectory starting at any point (w_{1o}, w_{2o}) approaches the origin as shown in Figure II-2a. This configuration is called a "stable" node. In the case where λ_1 and λ_2 are both positive, the point $(w_1(t), w_2(t))$ tends away from the origin as $t \to \infty$. The configuration of trajectories, shown in Figure II-2b, is the same as Figure II-2a except that the arrow directions are reversed; this is called an "unstable" node. Similar behavior is observed in the case of the Jordan form: μ negative corresponds to a stable node and μ positive corresponds to an unstable node.

Saddle: Let λ_1 and λ_2 have opposite signs, in particular $\lambda_1 < 0 < \lambda_2$. In this case, $|w_1(t)| \to 0$, $|w_2(t)| \to \infty$ as $t \to \infty$. The motion of the point $(w_1(t), w_2(t))$ is directed towards the origin along the w_1-axis and away from the origin along the w_2-axis. This configuration of trajectories is called a saddle as shown in Figure II-2c. A similar configuration of trajectories arises in the case $\lambda_2 < 0 < \lambda_1$.

Focus: Let the eigenvalues of the matrix A be complex conjugate, taking the values $\alpha \pm j\beta$; then TAT^{-1} has the form

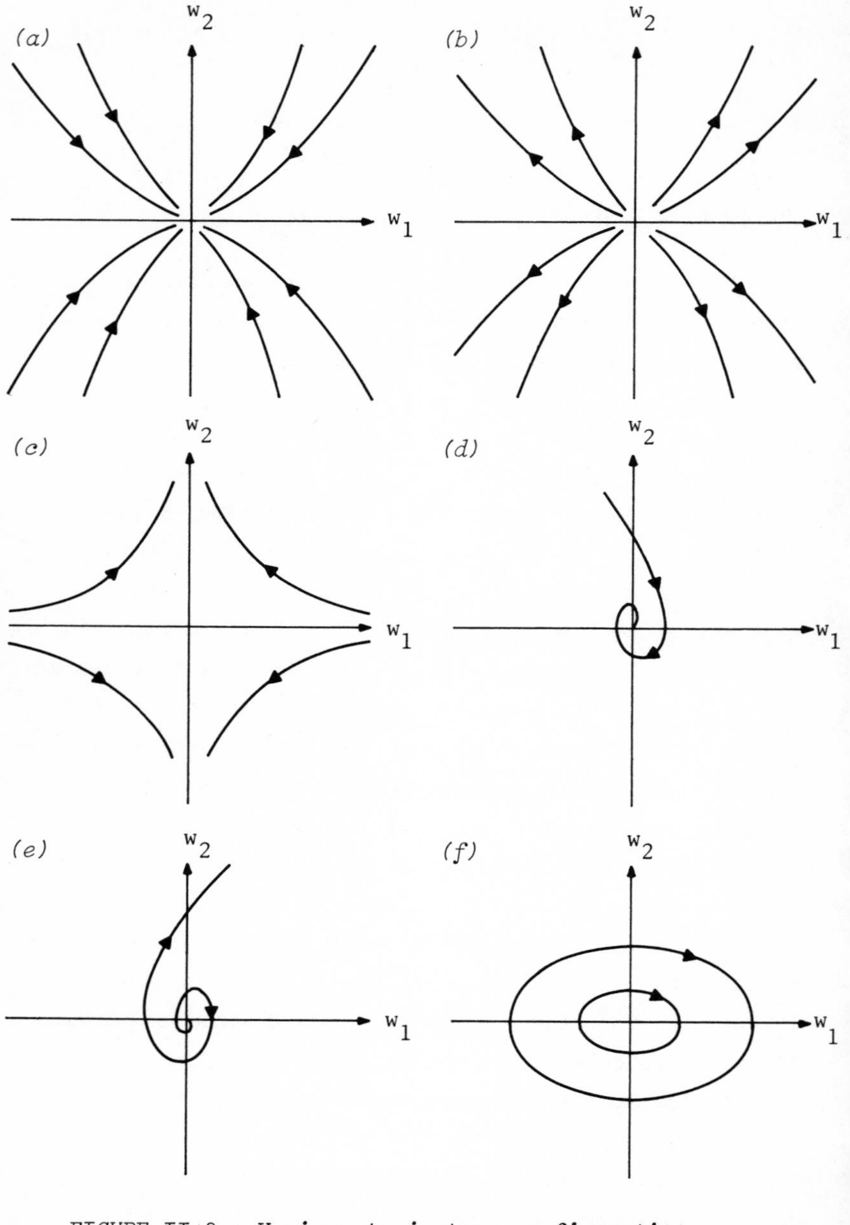

FIGURE II-2: Various trajectory configurations.

(c) given above. This configuration is best studied in polar coordinates. Let

$$w_1 = R \cos \phi$$

$$w_2 = R \sin \phi \quad ;$$

then

$$\dot{R} = \alpha R$$

$$\dot{\phi} = \beta \quad ,$$

and the solution to these differential equations is given by

$$R = R_o e^{\alpha t}$$

$$\phi = \beta t + \phi_o \quad ,$$

where R_o and ϕ_o are initial conditions for R and ϕ, respectively. The following three cases arise, depending upon α:

$R(t) \to 0$ as	$t \to \infty$,	$\alpha < 0$	stable spiral (stable focus)
$\lvert R(t) \rvert \to \infty$ as	$t \to \infty$,	$\alpha > 0$	unstable spiral (unstable focus)
$R(t) = R_o$ for all t	,	$\alpha = 0$	center.

Center is a degenerate case of spiral. These configurations are shown in Figure II-2d, 2e, 2f. The behaviors of trajectories in the neighborhood of the singular point for the stable node and stable spiral are similar. The distinguishing feature is the limiting behavior of $\phi(t)$ as $t \to \infty$. For the spiral, $\phi(t) \to \infty$ as $t \to \infty$, and for the node, $\phi(t) \to$ some ϕ^* as $t \to \infty$. The configurations shown in Figure II-2 are plotted in the (w_1,w_2)-plane. The corresponding configurations in the (z_1, z_2)-plane are similar but distorted.

The results above may be summarized as follows:

	$\lambda_1, \lambda_2 > 0$	unstable node
(a)	$\lambda_1, \lambda_2 < 0$	stable node
	$\lambda_1 < 0 < \lambda_2$ or $\lambda_2 < 0 < \lambda_1$	saddle
(b)	$\mu > 0$	unstable node
	$\mu < 0$	stable node
	$\alpha > 0$	unstable spiral
(c)	$\alpha < 0$	stable spiral
	$\alpha = 0$	center

Special Directions: Certain straight lines in the phase plane have important properties and these properties are helpful in drawing phase-plane plots.

Line along which $\dot{z}_1 = 0$ or $\dot{z}_2 = 0$: Along the line $a_{11}z_1 + a_{12}z_2 = 0$, *i.e.*, $\dot{z}_1 = 0$, the trajectories are moving parallel to z_2-axis; and along the line $a_{21}z_1+a_{22}z_2 = 0$, *i.e.*, $\dot{z}_2 = 0$, the trajectories are moving parallel to z_1-axis.

It may be observed that the equations $\dot{z}_1 = 0$ and $\dot{z}_2 = 0$ cannot hold simultaneously except at the origin, since the origin is an isolated singularity. A typical situation is shown in Figure II-3a. The direction of the arrows is determined by evaluating the non-zero derivative.

Line along which $\dot{r} = 0$: Let $z_1 = r \cos \theta$ and $z_2 = r \sin \theta$; then from (16),

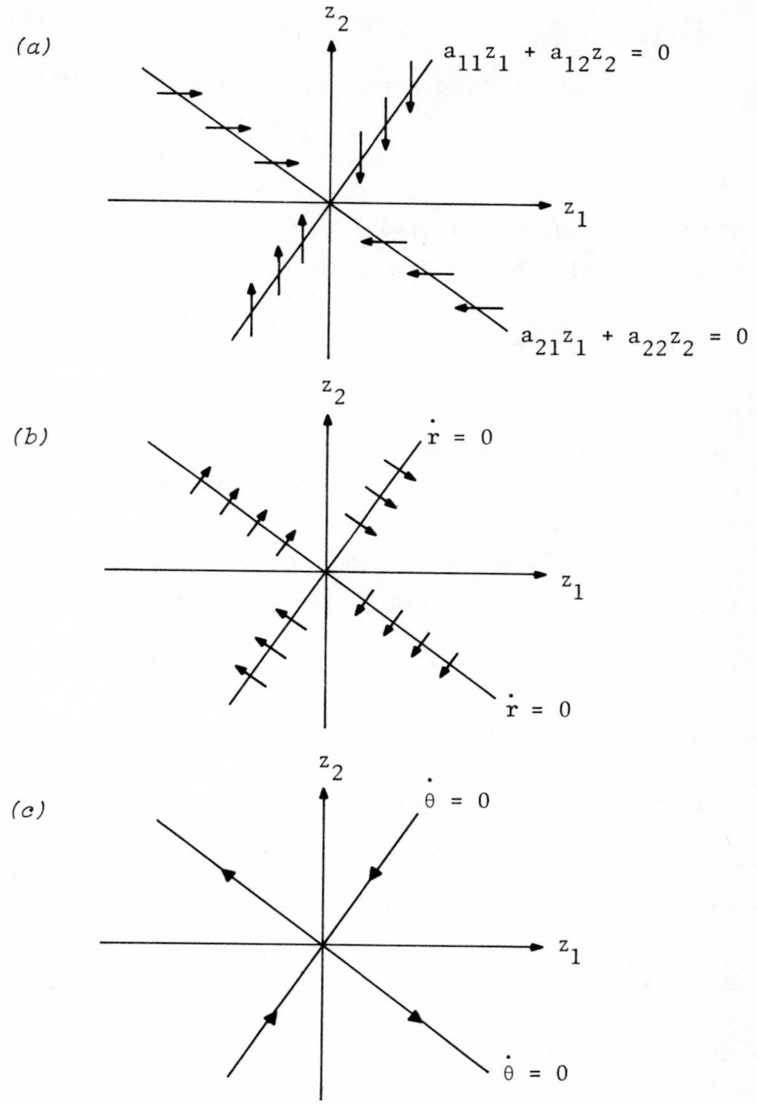

FIGURE II-3: Special directions of trajectories.

$$\dot{r} = r[a_{11}\cos^2\theta + (a_{12} + a_{21})\sin\theta\ \cos\theta + a_{22}\ \sin^2\theta]. \quad (22)$$

The directions along which $\dot{r} = 0$ are given by the equation

$$a_{11}\cos^2\theta + (a_{12} + a_{21})\sin\theta\ \cos\theta + a_{22}\ \sin^2\theta = 0\ . \quad (23)$$

If $\theta = \theta_o$ is a solution to (23), then $\theta = \pi+\theta_o$ is also a solution to (23). Equation (23) may be reduced to

$$\tan\theta = [-(a_{12} + a_{21}) \pm \sqrt{(a_{12}+a_{21})^2 - 4a_{11}a_{22}}\ ]/2a_{22}\ .$$

When $(a_{12}+a_{21})^2 - 4a_{11}a_{22} \geq 0$, there are real directions at which r goes through maxima or minima. A typical situation is shown in Figure II-3b. The direction of the arrows is determined by evaluating $\dot{\theta}$.

Line along which $\dot{\theta} = 0$: Again using the transformation $z_1 = r\cos\theta$, $z_2 = r\sin\theta$, the equations (16) give:

$$\dot{\theta} = a_{21}\cos^2\theta + (a_{22}-a_{11})\sin\theta\ \cos\theta - a_{12}\ \sin^2\theta. \quad (24)$$

Zeros of $\dot{\theta}$ are given by

$$a_{21}\cos^2\theta + (a_{22}-a_{11})\sin\theta\ \cos\theta - a_{12}\ \sin^2\theta = 0\ . \quad (25)$$

Here again, if $\theta = \theta_o$ is a solution to (25) then $\theta = \pi+\theta_o$ is also a solution. Equation (25) may be reduced to

$$\tan\theta = [(a_{22}-a_{11}) \pm \sqrt{(a_{22}-a_{11})^2 + 4a_{21}a_{12}}\ ]/2a_{12}.$$

If $(a_{22}-a_{11})^2 + 4a_{21}a_{12} \geq 0$, real directions along which $\dot{\theta} = 0$ may be obtained. A typical situation is shown in Figure II-3c where the arrow directions are obtained by evaluating $\dot{r}$. Two important observations may be made for lines along which $\dot{\theta} = 0$. They are given as exercises below.

Exercise 2: Show that $\theta = \theta_o$ and $\theta = \pi+\theta_o$ are trajectories for the system (16), where θ_o is a solution for (25).

Exercise 3: Let $\tan \theta_{o1} = \hat{z}_1$, $\tan \theta_{o2} = \hat{z}_2$, $\tan \theta = \hat{z}$, where θ_{o1}, θ_{o2} are the solutions to (25) and $\hat{z} = z_2/z_1$. Show that

$$\left|\frac{\hat{z}-\hat{z}_2}{\hat{z}-\hat{z}_1}\right| = C \exp(t \sqrt{(a_{22}-a_{11})^2 + 4a_{12}a_{21}})$$

$$\text{or} \quad = C \exp(-t \sqrt{(a_{22}-a_{11})^2 + 4a_{12}a_{21}}) \quad ,$$

where C is a constant. Also, determine the asymptotic behavior of $\hat{z}$ as $t \to \infty$ or $t \to -\infty$.

Example: The circuit shown in Figure II-4, containing a linear resistance, inductance and capacitance in series, is characterized by the differential equation

$$L\ddot{q} + R\dot{q} + (1/C)q = 0 \quad , \tag{26}$$

where q is the charge. Let $i = \dot{q}$, then the circuit is described by

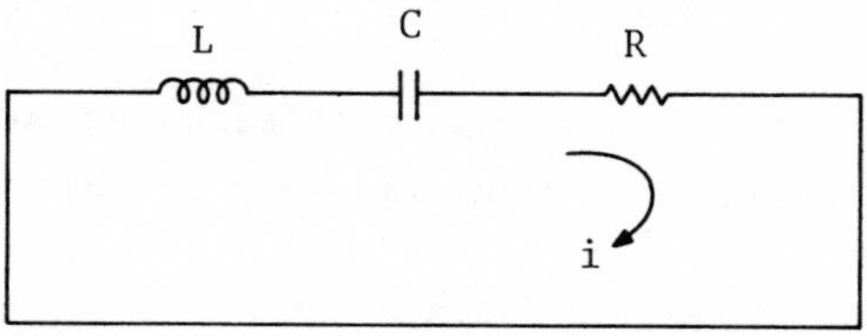

FIGURE II-4: A linear electrical circuit.

$$\dot{q} = i$$
$$\dot{i} = -2\beta i - w_o^2 q \quad , \tag{27}$$

where $2\beta = R/L$, $w_o^2 = 1/LC$. The eigenvalues of the system are

$$\lambda_1, \lambda_2 = -\beta \pm \sqrt{\beta^2 - w_o^2} \quad . \tag{28}$$

If $\beta > 0$, the singular point is a stable node or spiral, depending upon whether $\beta^2 \geq w_o^2$ or $\beta^2 < w_o^2$. In either of the two cases, the singular point is a stable singular point. If $\beta < 0$, the singular point is an unstable node or spiral. If $\beta = 0$, the singular point is a center.

Exercise 4: The motion of a simple pendulum with damping is described by

$$\ddot{\theta} + \varepsilon\dot{\theta} + k \sin \theta = 0 \ , \quad k > 0, \ \varepsilon > 0 \ .$$

Find the singular points, linearize the system about these points, and discuss the nature of the singular points.

Exercise 5: Discuss the nature of singular points for Volterra's growth equations for competing populations.

Exercise 6: Discuss the nature of singular points for Rapoport's equations for an arms race between two nations.

3. *Nonlinear Second-Order Systems*

The behavior of a linear second-order system (16) is related to its nonlinear counterpart (14) by a variety of results. One arrives at different results depending upon the nature of assumptions on the strength of the nonlinearity. A weak but nevertheless quite useful result will be stated below, and it will be proved for the case of a stable spiral. For details of the proofs concerning other cases and for proofs of different results, the reader is recommended to consult Coddington and Levinson [1], Nemytskii and Stepanov [1] and Lefschetz [1].

Theorem: The structures of the trajectories in the neighborhood of the singular point at the origin for the linear differential equation $\dot{z} = Az$ and the nonlinear differential equation $\dot{y} = Ay + Y^*(y)$ are similar in the cases of node, spiral and saddle, *i.e.*,

Linear System	Nonlinear System
node	node
spiral	spiral
saddle	saddle

provided that

$$Y^*(y) = \begin{bmatrix} Y_1^*(y_1, y_2) \\ Y_2^*(y_1, y_2) \end{bmatrix} = \begin{bmatrix} o(y_1^2 + y_2^2) \\ 0(y_1^2 + y_2^2) \end{bmatrix} .$$

Proof: Let the origin for the linear system be a stable spiral, *i.e.*, $\alpha < 0$, $\beta > 0$. In this case the linear system may be transformed to polar coordinates, giving

$$\dot{R} = \alpha R$$

$$\dot{\phi} = \beta \quad .$$

The behavior of the solution is described by $R(t) \to 0$, $\phi(t) \to \infty$ as $t \to \infty$. On the application of the same transformations to the nonlinear system, the system reduces to

$$\dot{\tilde{R}} = \alpha\tilde{R} + \eta_1(\tilde{R}, \tilde{\phi})$$

$$\dot{\tilde{\phi}} = \beta + \eta_2(\tilde{R}, \tilde{\phi}) \quad ,$$

where $\eta_1(\tilde{R}, \tilde{\phi}) = O(\tilde{R}^2)$ and $\eta_2(\tilde{R}, \tilde{\phi}) = O(\tilde{R})$. Now one may choose R^* such that

$$|\eta_1(\tilde{R}, \tilde{\phi})| \leq |\alpha\tilde{R}|$$

$$|\eta_2(\tilde{R}, \tilde{\phi})| \leq \beta^* < \beta \quad ,$$

for $\tilde{R} < R^*$. If the initial conditions are within the disc of radius R^*, then it is easily seen that $\tilde{R} \to 0$ and $\phi(t) \to \infty$ as $t \to \infty$. Similar proofs may be given for the cases of nodes and saddle points. ◆

In the case of a center, no such statement as the theorem above exists, as may be seen from the following example:

$$\dot{x}_1 = \beta x_2 + \mu x_1(x_1^2 + x_2^2)$$

$$\dot{x}_2 = -\beta x_1 + \mu x_2(x_1^2 + x_2^2) \quad .$$

The linearized system is described by

$$\dot{x}_1 = \beta x_2$$

$$\dot{x}_2 = -\beta x_1 \quad ,$$

and the structure of the trajectories corresponds to a center. However, the nonlinear system may be reduced to

$$\dot{R} = \mu R^3$$

$$\dot{\phi} = \beta \quad ,$$

and the system is an unstable or a stable spiral depending upon the sign of μ. This behavior cannot be deduced from the linearized equations.

It should be observed that the weaker condition of $Y_1^*(y_1,y_2)$, $Y_2^*(y_1,y_2) = o(\sqrt{y_1^2 + y_2^2}\,)$, as $y_1,y_2 \to 0$, does not imply that a node structure is preserved. For example, consider the system

$$\dot{x}_1 = -x_1 - 2x_2/\log(x_1^2 + x_2^2)$$

$$\dot{x}_2 = -x_2 + 2x_1/\log(x_1^2 + x_2^2) \quad .$$

In polar coordinates, this system is described by

$$\dot{R} = -R$$

$$\dot{\phi} = 1/\log R \quad .$$

The linearized system is a node and the nonlinear system is a spiral.

In the discussion above, the behavior of trajectories in the neighborhood of simple singularities has been discussed. The nature of the trajectories is rather complex if the singularity is non-simple. The reader is recommended to consult Nemytskii and Stepanov [1], Aggarwal [1,2], Forster [1], Cronin [1], Shapovalov [1], and Lefschetz [2] for information on non-simple singularities.

4. *Global Phase-Plane Analysis*

The local structure of the trajectories is similar for linear and nonlinear systems under suitable assumptions on the nonlinearity. This enables the plotting of phase-plane trajectories in the neighborhood of the singular points. If the nonlinear system has several singular points, one may plot trajectories in the neighborhood of each of these singular points. Under certain circumstances, it is possible to construct the trajectories for the entire phase plane from the knowledge of trajectories in the neighborhood of all singular points. This is illustrated by the following example.

Example: The equation of motion for a pendulum is described by

$$\ddot{\theta} + k \sin \theta = 0 \quad ,$$

where $k > 0$ is a constant. Choose $\dot{\theta} = v$, the system equations are

$$\dot{\theta} = v$$

$$v = -k \sin \theta \quad .$$

The singular points for the system are at $(n\pi, 0)$, $n = 0, \pm 1, \pm 2, \ldots$. Using the transformation

$$\phi = \theta - n\pi \quad ,$$

one obtains

$$\dot{\phi} = v$$

$$\dot{v} = (-1)^{n+1} k \sin \phi \quad .$$

In the neighborhood of the singular point, the equations are given by

$$\dot{\phi} = v$$

$$\dot{v} = (-1)^{n+1} k \phi \quad ,$$

which gives a saddle point if n is odd and a center if n is

even. By observing that (i) the trajectories do not intersect (except at the singular points) because the solution is unique, (ii) trajectories of the linear system approximate the behavior of the trajectories of the nonlinear system in the neighborhood of the singular points, (iii) the trajectories are continuous curves, and (iv) centers do not degenerate into spirals, one obtains the complete phase-plane portrait as shown in Figure II-5. There are cases where the non-intersecting property of trajectories is insufficient to obtain a complete phase-plane portrait, and

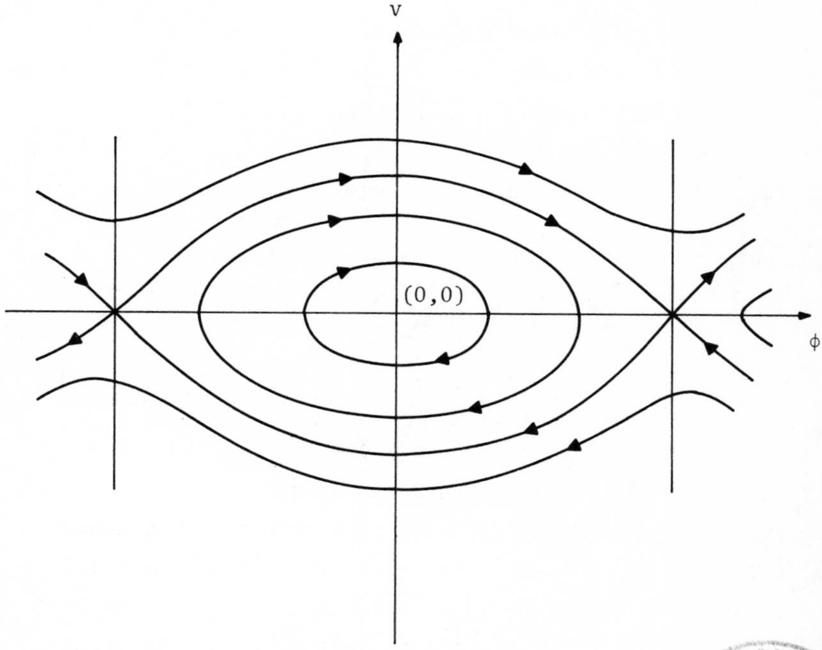

FIGURE II-5: Phase-plane portrait for the simple pendulum.

one must use the defining equations to complete the portrait. The case of a rotating pendulum (Exercise 9) is a good example. The singular points are saddles and centers, and they are interlaced. However, for the rotating pendulum there are two types of closed trajectories: (i) enclosing a center and (ii) enclosing two centers and a saddle.

The techniques above may be applied to piecewise-linear systems, a special class of nonlinear systems, with considerable advantage. The procedure consists of the following steps: (i) subdivide the phase plane into regions within each of which the trajectories are those of a linear system; (ii) assign singular points to each region; (iii) determine the nature of the singular points; (iv) connect the trajectories belonging to various regions to obtain the complete phase-plane portrait. An example follows to illustrate the procedure above.

Example: Consider the piecewise-linear system

$$\dot{x}_1 = x_2$$

$$\dot{x}_2 = -f(x_2) - 3x_1 \quad ,$$

where $f(x_2) = 4x_2$, $x_2 \geq 0$; $f(x_2) = -2x_2$ for $x_2 < 0$. For $x_2 < 0$ the system is an unstable spiral, and for $x_2 \geq 0$ the system is a stable node. The composite trajectories are shown in Figure II-6. This composite phase-plane plot is obtained by adjoining the phase-plane plot for the stable node for $x_2 \geq 0$ and the phase-plane plot for the unstable spiral for $x_2 < 0$. It may be observed from the composite phase-plane plot that the singularity at the origin is a stable one. Also, the slope of trajectories at $x_2 = 0$ is

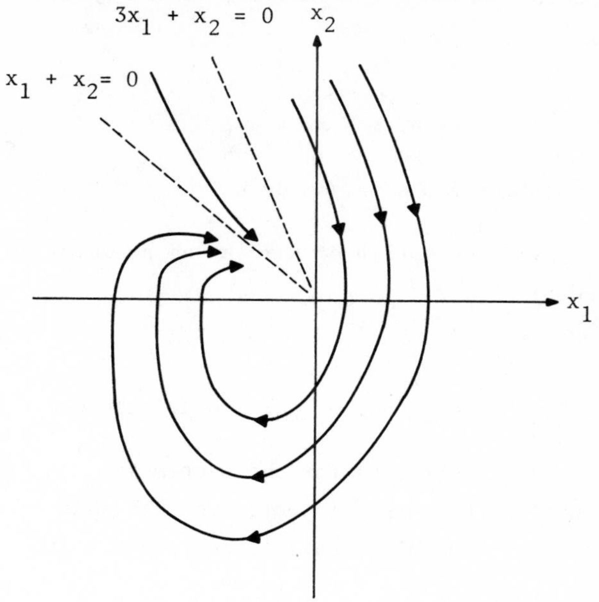

FIGURE II-6: Phase-plane portrait for a piecewise-linear system.

continuous. Kalman [1] gives several additional examples where the procedure above may be used with advantage.

Exercise 7: Rayleigh's differential equation,

$$\dot{x}_1 = x_2$$

$$\dot{x}_2 = -\varepsilon(x_2^3/3 - x_2) - x_1 \quad ,$$

has a singular point at the origin. Find the nature of the singular point, sketch the trajectories in the neighborhood of the singular point, and compare the behavior of the linearized and nonlinear systems at the origin.

Exercise 8: Discuss the behavior of the system:

$$\dot{x}_1 = x_2$$

$$\dot{x}_2 = -k - x_1 + k(1 - x_1)^{-3} \quad ,$$

as a function of the parameter k.

Exercise 9: The motion of a rotating pendulum is described by

$$\dot{\theta} = w$$

$$\dot{w} = (\cos\theta - \lambda)\sin\theta, \quad \lambda > 0 \quad .$$

Sketch the trajectories for the system and compare the configuration of these trajectories with that of the simple pendulum (see Hint above (p.30) and Minorsky [1]).

Exercise 10: Sketch trajectories for Volterra's growth equations.

Exercise 11: Sketch trajectories for Rapoport's arms race equations.

Exercise 12: Show that the singular point at the origin for the system

$$\dot{x}_1 = x_1 \sin\frac{1}{x_1}$$

$$\dot{x}_2 = x_2 \quad ,$$

is not an isolated singular point.

Exercise 13: Show that the singular point at the origin for the system

$$\dot{x}_1 = ax_1^2 + bx_2^2$$

$$\dot{x}_2 = cx_1^2 + dx_2^2 \quad ,$$

$ad - bc \neq 0$ is an isolated singular point but not a simple singular point.

Exercise 14: Draw a phase-plane plot for the motion of the damped pendulum.

CHAPTER III

STABILITY OF NONLINEAR SYSTEMS

1. *Definition of Stability*

The concept of "stability of a system" is a complicated one, and the situation is made more difficult by the several different colloquial usages of the term "stability." The stability of a singular point of a second-order time-invariant system has been already defined in Chapter II. This notion of stability will be made more precise in the following, and several definitions and illustrations of the different forms of stability will be presented.

The term "stability" will be defined in the context of the system

$$\dot{y} = Y(y,t) \quad , \tag{1}$$

where y is an n-vector and $Y(0,t) = 0$ for all t. (There is no loss of generality in assuming the origin to be the singular or equilibrium point of the system.) The problem of stability of a trajectory may also be reduced to the problem of stability of an equilibrium point by the following method. Let the system be described by

$$\dot{x} = X(x,t) \quad , \tag{2}$$

and let $\hat{x}(t)$ be a particular solution of the system. The stability of the solution $\hat{x}(t)$ may be studied by considering the deviation of a solution $x(t)$ from the solution $\hat{x}(t)$.

Let

$$x(t) = \hat{x}(t) + y(t) . \tag{3}$$

Then,

$$\dot{x}(t) = \dot{\hat{x}}(t) + \dot{y}(t)$$

$$= X(\hat{x}(t) + y(t), t) .$$

On expanding the function $X(\hat{x}(t) + y(t), t)$ about the solution $\hat{x}(t)$ for every t, the differential equation for x(t) becomes

$$\dot{x}(t) = X(\hat{x}(t), t) + Y(y(t), t) ,$$

where $Y(y,t)$ is the remainder after the first term $X(\hat{x}(t),t)$. Using the fact that $\dot{\hat{x}} = X(\hat{x},t)$, one obtains

$$\dot{y} = Y(y,t) ,$$

and it is clear that $Y(0,t) \equiv 0$. Thus, the study of the stability of $\hat{x}(\cdot)$ of (2) is equivalent to studying the stability of the trivial solution of (1). In other words, the stability of a trajectory has been reduced to the stability of an equilibrium point.

Example: Consider the system

$$\dot{x}_1 = x_2$$

$$\dot{x}_2 = -x_2(x_1^2-1)-x_1 + 2 \sin 3t .$$

A solution of the system is given by

$$\hat{x}_1 = -2 \cos t$$

$$\hat{x}_2 = 2 \sin t .$$

On applying the transformation,

$$x_1(t) = y_1(t) - 2\cos t$$

$$x_2(t) = y_2(t) + 2\sin t \quad ,$$

the system equations reduce to

$$\dot{y}_1(t) = y_2$$

$$\dot{y}_2(t) = -y_2(4\cos^2 t - 1 + y_1^2 - 4y_1\cos t) - y_1(1 - 8\sin t\cos t + 2y_1\sin t)$$

or

$$\begin{bmatrix} \dot{y}_1 \\ \dot{y}_2 \end{bmatrix} = \begin{bmatrix} 0 & 1 \\ -1+8\cos t\sin t & 1-4\cos^2 t \end{bmatrix} \begin{bmatrix} y_1 \\ y_2 \end{bmatrix} + \begin{bmatrix} 0 \\ -y_1^2 y_2 + 4y_1 y_2\cos t - 2y_1^2\sin t \end{bmatrix} .$$

Thus the stability of the particular solution may be studied by considering the stability of the trivial solution of the transformed equations.

In the following, the solution to the system (1), with initial condition y_0 at $t = t_0$, is denoted by $y(t,y_0,t_0)$. The norm of the vector y will be denoted by $\|y\|$. Without loss of generality, this norm will be assumed to be

$$\|y\| = \sum_{i=1}^{n} |y_i| \quad .$$

The norm for a matrix $A = (a_{ij})$ will be given by

$$\|A\| = \sum_{i,j=1}^{n} |a_{ij}| \quad .$$

The symbol ' denotes the transpose of a real vector or matrix, and the complex conjugate transpose for a complex vector or matrix.

The definition of the stability of a singular point of a second-order system given in Chapter II may be paraphrased as follows: A singular point is stable provided that, for any given circle in the phase plane enclosing the singular point, called the ε-circle, there is another circle enclosing the singular point, called the δ-circle, such that any trajectory starting within the δ-circle is confined within the ε-circle for all $t \geq t_0$. This definition agrees with the colloquial usage of the word stability, *i.e.*, if small perturbations to the system at the singular point stay small, the system is stable.

The definition of stability for time-varying systems or higher-order systems is a generalization of the earlier definition; however, one defines the concept of stability and uniform stability as follows:

Definition: Stable. The equilibrium point at the origin for the system (1) is said to be stable if, for every $\varepsilon > 0$ and any t_0, there exists $\delta(\varepsilon, t_0) > 0$ such that $\|y_0\| < \delta$ implies that $\|y(t, y_0, t_0)\| \leq \varepsilon$, for every $t \geq t_0$.

Definition: Uniformly stable. The equilibrium point at the origin for the system (1) is said to be uniformly stable if for every $\varepsilon > 0$, there exists $\delta(\varepsilon) > 0$ such that for every $\|y_0\| < \delta$, and all t_0, $\|y(t, y_0, t_0)\| \leq \varepsilon$ for every $t \geq t_0$.

In the case of time-invariant systems, the notions of "stability" and "uniform stability" are identical, so the definition given in the context of singular-point analysis agrees with the definition above. A center is such an equilibrium point. A stable node exhibits a stronger notion of stability called asymptotic stability.

Definition: Asymptotically stable. The equilibrium point at the origin for the system (1) is said to be asymptotically stable if (i) the origin is stable; (ii) there is a real function $\tilde{\delta}(t_0)$ such that for all $\|y_0\| < \tilde{\delta}(t_0)$, $y(t,y_0,t_0) \to 0$ as $t \to \infty$.

Definition: Uniformly asymptotically stable. The equilibrium point at the origin is uniformly asymptotically stable if the equilibrium point is (i) uniformly stable; (ii) there is a constant $\tilde{\delta}$ such that for all $\|y_0\| < \tilde{\delta}$, $y(t,y_0,t_0) \to 0$ as $t \to \infty$.

Stability and asymptotic stability are essentially local notions since one is interested in the behavior of the system in a sufficiently small neighborhood of the equilibrium point. Also, it must be emphasized that a system may be unstable and still have $y(t,y_0,t_0) \to 0$ as $t \to \infty$ for every y_0. A complicated example due to Birkhoff and Rota [1] illustrates this behavior. Therefore, the inclusion of stability of the equilibrium point in the definition of asymptotic stability is important and not redundant. The concept of global stability is defined as follows:

Definition: Uniform asymptotic stability in the large. The equilibrium point at the origin for the system (1) is said to be uniformly asymptotically stable in the large if

(i) the origin is uniformly asymptotically stable;

(ii) for every $\eta > 0$, there exists $\psi(\eta)$ such that $\|y_0\| \leq \eta$ implies $\|y(t,y_0,t_0)\| < \psi(\eta)$ for all $t \geq t_0$;

(iii) for every y_0, $y(t,y_0,t_0) \to 0$ as $t \to \infty$.

The notion of uniform asymptotic stability in the

large is the strongest form of stability. To paraphrase the above definition, it implies that the equilibrium point is uniformly stable, all solutions are uniformly bounded, and all solutions starting with arbitrarily large initial conditions will approach the equilibrium point as $t \to \infty$. Obviously, this is a global notion, and excludes the existence of any other equilibrium points for the system, stable or unstable.

There are several other forms of stability which differ from the above in subtle ways. Interested readers are recommended to consult the excellent survey paper by Kalman and Bertram [1]. Before we tackle the problem of stability of nonlinear systems, it will be best for us to investigate the simpler problem of the stability of linear systems.

2. *Stability of Linear Systems*

Consider the system

$$\dot{z} = Az \quad , \tag{4}$$

where z is an n-vector and A is a constant n×n matrix. The equilibrium points of the system are given by solutions of the linear algebraic equation $Az = 0$, including the trivial solution $z = 0$. If one is interested in the stability of an equilibrium point besides the one at the origin, then a simple transformation, similar to the one used for second-order systems, reduces the problem to the study of the stability of the equilibrium point at the origin. The solution of (4) is given by

$$z(t) = e^{A(t-t_o)} z_o \quad , \tag{5}$$

where z_o is the initial condition at $t = t_o$.

In the following, the relationship between the location of the eigenvalues of the matrix A and the stability of the system (4) will be investigated. To do this, consider the transformation T,

$$w = Tz \quad ,$$

where T is a nonsingular n×n matrix. The differential equation for w is given by

$$\dot{w} = TAT^{-1} w \quad .$$

It is known that by a suitable choice of T, TAT^{-1} may be reduced to

$$J = \begin{bmatrix} J_0 & & & 0 \\ & J_1 & & \\ & & \ddots & \\ 0 & & & J_m \end{bmatrix}$$

where

$$J_0 = \begin{bmatrix} \lambda_1 & & 0 \\ & \ddots & \\ 0 & & \lambda_{m_0} \end{bmatrix}$$

and J_i is an $m_i \times m_i$ matrix having the form

$$\begin{bmatrix} \lambda_{m_0+i} & 1 & & 0 \\ & \ddots & \ddots & \\ & & \ddots & 1 \\ 0 & & & \lambda_{m_0+i} \end{bmatrix} \quad , \quad i = 1,\ldots,m \quad .$$

The eigenvalues $\lambda_1,\ldots,\lambda_{m_0}$ are of multiplicity one, and the eigenvalue λ_{m_0+i} is of multiplicity $m_i > 1$, $i = 1,\ldots,m$. (It may happen that in a particular case J_0 is not present.) It is easily seen that

$$e^{Jt} = \begin{bmatrix} e^{J_0 t} & & & 0 \\ & e^{J_1 t} & & \\ & & \ddots & \\ 0 & & & e^{J_m t} \end{bmatrix}$$

$$e^{J_0 t} = \begin{bmatrix} e^{\lambda_1 t} & & & 0 \\ & e^{\lambda_2 t} & & \\ & & \ddots & \\ 0 & & & e^{\lambda_{m_0} t} \end{bmatrix}$$

and

$$e^{J_i t} = \begin{bmatrix} 1 & t & \frac{t^2}{2!} & \cdots & \frac{t^{m_i-1}}{(m_i-1)!} \\ 0 & 1 & t & \ddots & \\ & & & & \ddots \\ 0 & 0 & 0 & & 1 \end{bmatrix} e^{\lambda_{m_0+i} t} \qquad i = 1,\ldots,m.$$

If the real part of each of the eigenvalues is less than zero, *i.e.*, all the eigenvalues lie in the open left half-plane, then each term of the matrix $\exp[Jt]$ tends to zero as $t \to \infty$. This observation, together with the fact that

$$z = T^{-1} e^{J(t-t_0)} T z_0,$$

enables us to conclude the following theorem:

Theorem: If the eigenvalues of the matrix A are in the open left half-plane, then the equilibrium point at the origin for the system $\dot{z} = Az$ is asymptotically stable.

Exercise 1: Show that if a linear system is asymptotically stable, then the system is asymptotically stable in the large. In addition, show that if the system is time-invariant, then the system will be uniformly asymptotically stable in the large.

As seen above, the asymptotic behavior of the system depends upon the nature of the eigenvalues of the matrix A, or equivalently, the roots of the characteristic equation given by

$$\det (A - \lambda I) = 0 \quad , \tag{6}$$

where I is the identity matrix. By expanding the determinant, the characteristic equation may be written as

$$a_0 \lambda^n + a_1\lambda^{n-1} + \dots + a_{n-1}\lambda + a_n = 0 \quad .$$

The roots of the equation will be in the open left half-plane if and only if the determinants of all the principal minors of the n×n matrix

$$\Delta_n = \begin{bmatrix} a_1 & a_3 & a_5 & \cdots & 0 & 0 & 0 \\ a_0 & a_2 & a_4 & \cdots & \cdot & \cdot & \cdot \\ 0 & a_1 & a_3 & \cdots & & 0 & 0 \\ 0 & a_0 & a_2 & \cdots & & 0 & 0 \\ \cdot & \cdot & \cdot & & \cdot & \cdot & \cdot \\ \cdot & \cdot & \cdot & & a_{n-2} & a_n & 0 \\ \cdot & \cdot & \cdot & & a_{n-3} & a_{n-1} & 0 \\ 0 & 0 & 0 & \cdots & a_{n-4} & a_{n-2} & a_n \end{bmatrix} \tag{7}$$

are positive. This condition of positivity of all principal minors is known as the Routh [1]-Hurwitz [1] criterion. The proof of this classical result is omitted here; the proof is found in Gantmacher [1]. Several computationally more convenient forms of the above criterion have been developed recently, for example, see Jury and Ahn [1].

Exercise 2: Show that there exist constants R and C such that the solution to the system (4) satisfies the inequality

$$\|z(t,z_0,t_0)\| \leq Re^{-C(t-t_0)} .$$

Exercise 3: Show that if the eigenvalues of A are in the open left half-plane, then the equilibrium point at the origin for the system

$$\dot{z} = (A + B(t))z$$

is uniformly asymptotically stable in the large provided that $\int_0^\infty \|B(t)\| dt < \infty$.

In the case when A(t) is a time-varying matrix, it is possible that the eigenvalues of the matrix are in the open left half-plane for every t, and yet the system is unstable. An example of this due to Markus and Yamabe [1] is given in the following as Exercise 4.

Exercise 4: Show that for the system

$$\dot{y} = \begin{bmatrix} -1 + a\cos^2 t & 1 - a\sin t\cos t \\ -1 - a\sin t\cos t & -1 + a\sin^2 t \end{bmatrix} y,$$

the solution is given by

$$y = \begin{bmatrix} e^{(a-1)t}\cos t & e^{-t}\sin t \\ -e^{(a-1)t}\sin t & e^{-t}\cos t \end{bmatrix} y_0 \quad ,$$

and that the system is asymptotically stable if $0 < a < 1$, unstable for $1 < a < 2$, whereas the eigenvalues of the system are in the open left half-plane for $0 < a < 2$.

However, when $A(t)$ is periodic, a result similar to that of Exercise 3 is feasible. Let $A(t)$ be periodic with period T; then the solution to the system (4) may be expressed as

$$z(t) = P(t,t_0)e^{Q(t-t_0)} z_0 \quad ,$$

where $P(t,t_0)$ is periodic with period T and Q is a constant matrix. It is the property above that makes the following result of Exercise 5 possible. The proof of the result above is found in Desoer [1].

Exercise 5: If the system

$$\dot{z} = A(t)z \quad ,$$

is uniformly asymptotically stable in the large, then the system

$$\dot{y} = (A(t) + B(t))y \quad ,$$

is also uniformly asymptotically stable in the large provided that (i) $A(t)$ is periodic; and (ii) $\int_0^\infty \|B(t)\|\,dt < \infty$.

3. *Local Stability of Nonlinear Systems*

In the case of second-order systems, it is found that

the structures of trajectories in the neighborhood of the equilibrium point for the linear and nonlinear systems are related. A similar result is true for n*th*-order systems. Here, one is interested in the stability of the equilibrium point rather than the detailed structure of trajectories.

Theorem: If the system

$$\dot{z} = Az \quad ,$$

is asymptotically stable in the large, then the system

$$\dot{y} = Ay + f(y) \quad , \tag{9}$$

is asymptotically stable if

(i) A is a constant matrix;

(ii) $f(\cdot)$ is continuous in some neighborhood of the origin;

(iii) $\|f(y)\|/\|y\| \to 0$ as $\|y\| \to 0$.

Proof: By a suitable choice of a linear transformation T, *i.e.*, $z = T^{-1}w$, the linear system (4) reduces to

$$\dot{w} = TAT^{-1} w \quad , \tag{10}$$

where

$$TAT^{-1} = \begin{bmatrix} \lambda_1 & b_{12} & \cdots & b_{1n} \\ 0 & \lambda_2 & & b_{2n} \\ & & \ddots & \vdots \\ 0 & 0 & & \lambda_n \end{bmatrix} . \tag{11}$$

The λ's are the eigenvalues of the system, and $|b_{ij}| \leq \varepsilon$, where $\varepsilon > 0$ is any given number. The proof for the existence of such a transformation is given by Bellman [1]. However, the existence of the transformation should not be interpreted to mean that a matrix with repeated eigenvalues can be diagonalized in general, for the transformation depends upon ε.

Applying the same transformation to the nonlinear system (9), one obtains, componentwise,

$$\dot{\tilde{y}}_k = \lambda_k \tilde{y}_k + \sum_{j>k}^{n} b_{kj} \tilde{y}_j + \tilde{f}_k(\tilde{y}) \quad , \quad k = 1,\ldots,n,$$

where $\tilde{f}_k(\cdot)$ satisfies the same conditions as $f(\cdot)$.

Let

$$R^2 = \sum_{k=1}^{n} |\tilde{y}_k|^2 = \sum_{k=1}^{n} \tilde{y}_k{}'\tilde{y}_k \quad ,$$

$$\alpha = \max_i \{\text{Real part of } \lambda_i\} \quad .$$

On differentiating and simplifying, one obtains

$$\frac{1}{2}\frac{d}{dt}(R^2) \leq \alpha R^2 + \varepsilon \|\tilde{y}\|^2 + \|\tilde{y}\| \, \|\tilde{f}(\tilde{y})\| \; .$$

Observing that $\alpha < 0$, $\tilde{f}$ is continuous and $\|\tilde{f}(y)\|/\|y\| \to 0$ as $\|y\| \to 0$, it follows that $dR^2/dt < 0$, and the system is asymptotically stable. ◆

The argument above is similar to the one used in the case of second-order systems. Several other proofs are possible, depending upon the assumptions on f. Bellman [1] is an excellent reference on this subject.

Example: The asymptotic stability in the large of the scalar system $\dot{z} = \alpha z$ implies the asymptotic stability of the equilibrium point at the origin for nonlinear system $\dot{y} = \alpha y + \beta y^3$. The theorem above, in general, gives no information on the global properties of the nonlinear system.

In the present case, for $\beta > 0$, the nonlinear system has additional equilibrium points at $\pm(-\alpha/\beta)^{1/2}$, and, therefore, global behavior may not be deduced from the analysis above.

Exercise 6: Show that if the system

$$\dot{z} = A(t)z \quad , \tag{12}$$

is uniformly asymptotically stable in the large, then the equilibrium point at the origin is asymptotically stable for the system

$$\dot{y} = A(t)y + f(y) \quad , \tag{13}$$

provided that

(i) $A(t)$ is periodic;

(ii) $f(\cdot)$ is continuous in a neighborhood of the origin;

(iii) $\|f(y)\|/\|y\| \to 0$ as $\|y\| \to 0$.

Here again, the result above is critically dependent upon the matrix $A(t)$ being periodic. It is not sufficient that the system (12) be asymptotically stable for the asymptotic stability of the system (13). The following example illustrates the fact that a linear time-varying system is asymptotically stable, whereas the corresponding nonlinear system with $\|f(y)\|/\|y\| \to 0$ as $\|y\| \to 0$ is unstable.

Example: For the system

$$\dot{z} = Az = \begin{bmatrix} -a & 0 \\ 0 & (\sin\log t + \cos\log t) - 2a \end{bmatrix} z,$$

the solution is given by

$$z = \begin{bmatrix} e^{-at} & 0 \\ 0 & e^{(t \sin \log t - 2at)} \end{bmatrix} z_o ,$$

and the system is stable provided $a > \frac{1}{2}$. However, solution to the system

$$\dot{y} = Ay + \begin{bmatrix} 0 \\ y_1^2 \end{bmatrix} ,$$

is given by

$$y_1 = z_{1o}\, e^{-at}$$

$$y_2 = e^{t \sin \log t - 2ta} \left(z_{2o} + z_{1o}^2 \int_0^t e^{-t_1 \sin \log t_1} dt_1 \right),$$

and

$$y_2 \to 0 \text{ as } t \to \infty \text{ only if } z_{1o} = 0 .$$

Exercise 7: The motion of a mass m attached to a spring is described by

$$\begin{aligned} \dot{\theta} &= v \\ \dot{v} &= -g \sin \theta / r \\ \dot{r} &= w \\ \dot{w} &= g \cos \theta - k(r-a)/m , \end{aligned}$$

where k and a are constants of the spring, θ represents the inclination of the spring to the vertical and r gives the stretched length of the spring. Find the equilibrium points of the system and discuss the nature of equilibrium points.

Exercise 8: Show that the system

$$\dot{z} = Az = \begin{bmatrix} -a & 0 \\ 0 & (\sin \log t + \cos \log t) - 2a \end{bmatrix} z$$

is stable for $a > \frac{1}{2}$, whereas the system

$$\dot{y} = Ay + \begin{bmatrix} 0 \\ y_1^2 \end{bmatrix}$$

is unstable. (See Hint, page 47, and Perron [1].)

4. *Liapunov's Direct Method*

The principal idea of Liapunov's method is derived from the following intuitive reasoning. Consider an isolated system and let $y(t,y_o,t_o)$ be a solution to the system. Further, let $V(y(t,y_o,t_o))$ be the energy associated with the isolated system. If the derivative $dV(y)/dt$ is negative for all $y(t,y_o,t_o)$ except the equilibrium point, then it follows that energy of the system decreases as t increases; and finally the system will reach the equilibrium point. These ideas are well illustrated by the circuit shown in Figure III-1. The circuit equations are

$$\frac{dv}{dt} = i/C$$

$$\frac{di}{dt} = - iR/L - v/L \quad .$$

Let the solution be denoted by $(i(t), v(t))$ $= (i(t,i_o,v_o,t_o), v(t,i_o,v_o,t_o))$, where i_o and v_o are initial current and voltage, respectively. The energy of the system is

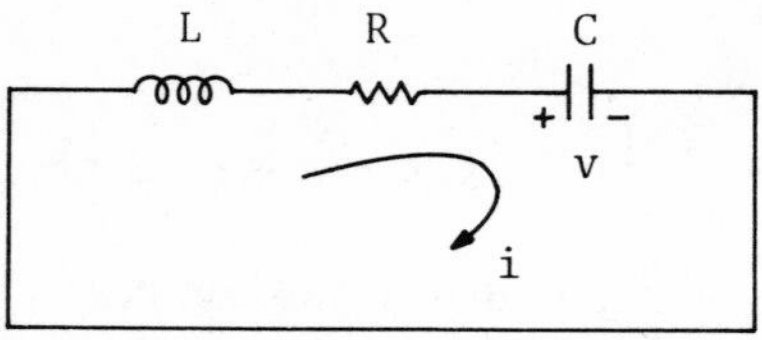

FIGURE III-1: Electrical circuit.

$$V(i(t),\ v(t)) = \frac{1}{2}\,Li^2(t) + \frac{1}{2}\,Cv^2(t) \quad ,$$

and the rate of change of energy is

$$\frac{dV(i(t),v(t))}{dt} = Li(t)\ \dot{i}(t) + Cv(t)\ \dot{v}(t) \quad .$$

Substituting for $\dot{i}(t)$ and $\dot{v}(t)$ from the circuit equations, one obtains

$$\frac{dV(i(t),v(t))}{dt} = -i^2(t)\ R \quad ,$$

which is due to the energy dissipated in the resistor R. By observing the fact that energy is being dissipated, one comes to the conclusion that the system will eventually reach the equilibrium point where $i = 0$ and $v = 0$. A visual analogy may be obtained by considering the surface

$$V = \frac{1}{2}\,Li^2 + \frac{1}{2}\,Cv^2 \quad .$$

This is a cup-shaped surface, as shown in Figure III-2. The constant-V loci are ellipses on the surface of the cup. If one starts the circuit with initial condition (i_o, v_o), and plots the trajectory on the surface shown, the point $(i(t), v(t))$ crosses the $V(i,v)$ = constant curves and moves towards the lowest point of the cup, which is the equilibrium point.

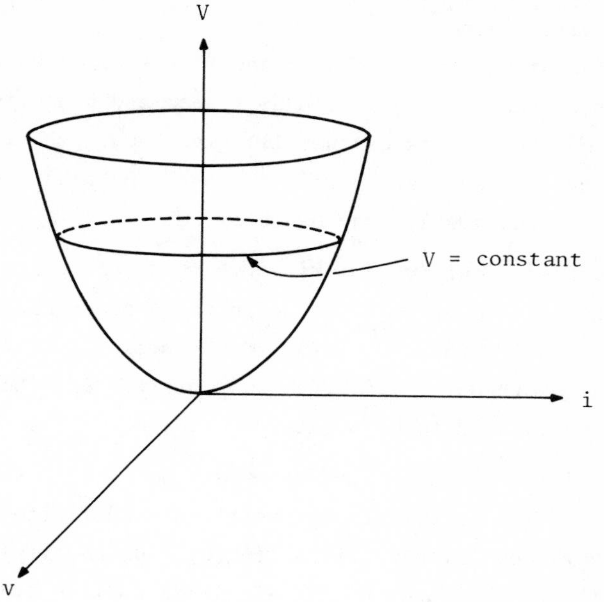

FIGURE III-2: Liapunov surface and constant-V curve.

In the example above, it was easy to associate the energy function V(i(t),v(t)) with the given circuit and therefore with the equations. However, given a set of equations describing a system, there is no obvious way of associating an energy function with the equations. In fact, the concept of energy may not be natural to a particular system, for example, a control system. Liapounoff [1] introduced and formalized the idea of using scalar functions besides the energy function associated with the system to investigate the stability of a system. The scalar function is now known as a Liapunov function, and the method of investigating stability using Liapunov functions is known as Liapunov's Direct Method.

The stability results of the last section were based upon the comparison of a linear system and a nonlinear system, and the results essentially give local stability. Liapunov's Direct Method uses a "test" function. Global as well as local results may be obtained.

Definition: Positive definite function. A scalar function $V(y)$ is said to be positive definite in a neighborhood η of the origin if $V(0) = 0$, $V(y) > 0$ whenever $y \neq 0$, and y is in the neighborhood η. If $-V(y)$ is positive definite, the function is said to be negative definite.

Definition: Positive semidefinite function. A scalar function $V(y)$ is said to be positive semidefinite in a neighborhood η of the origin if $V(0) = 0$, and $V(y) \geq 0$ with y in the neighborhood η. If $-V(y)$ is positive semidefinite, then the function is said to be negative semidefinite.

Liapunov's result in its simplest form is given by the following theorem. It is interesting to observe that the following theorem generalizes the idea of an energy function rather elegantly.

Stability theorem: The equilibrium point at the origin for the system

$$\dot{y} = Y(y) \quad , \tag{14}$$

is stable if there exists a positive definite scalar function $V(y)$ with continuous partial derivatives such that the derivative of $V(y)$ along the solution of (14), given by $\sum_{i=1}^{n} \frac{\partial V}{\partial y_i} \dot{y}_i$, is negative semidefinite in some neighborhood

η of the origin.

The derivative of the scalar function $V(y)$ along the solution of a differential system (1) or (14) will be denoted by $\dot{V}(y)$. At times the notation $\dot{V}(y(t,y_o,t_o))$ will be used to emphasize the evaluation of the derivative of $V(y)$ along the solution of the differential system.

Asymptotic stability theorem: The equilibrium point at the origin of the system (14) is asymptotically stable if there exists a positive definite scalar function $V(y)$ with continuous partial derivatives such that the derivative of $V(y)$ along the solution of (14), $\dot{V}(y)$, is negative definite in some neighborhood η of the origin.

A more general and useful result is the following theorem:

Uniform asymptotic stability in the large theorem: If there exists a scalar function $V(y)$ with continuous partial derivatives, and continuous scalar functions $a(r)$, $b(r)$, $c(r)$ such that

(i) $a(0) = b(0) = c(0) = 0$,

(ii) $a(r)$, $b(r)$ are non-decreasing and $0 < a(\|y\|) \leq V(y) \leq b(\|y\|)$, $y \neq 0$,

(iii) $c(r)$ is non-decreasing and the derivative of $V(y)$ along the solution of (1) satisfies $\dot{V}(y) \leq -c(\|y\|) < 0$, $y \neq 0$,

(iv) $a(r) \to \infty$ as $r \to \infty$,

then the equilibrium point at the origin for the system (1) is uniformly asymptotically stable in the large.

Proof: The condition $\dot{V}(y) \leq -c(\|y\|) < 0$ implies that $V(y)$ monotonically decreases along the solution of the system. Now for any given $\varepsilon > 0$, choose $\delta(\varepsilon) < b^{-1}(a(\varepsilon))$

where $b^{-1}(a(\varepsilon))$ is the smallest γ such that $b(\gamma) = a(\varepsilon)$. Then for $\|y_o\| < \delta(\varepsilon)$, the following series of inequalities holds:

$$\begin{aligned} a(\|y(t,y_o,t_o)\|) &\le V(y(t,y_o,t_o)) \le V(y(t_o,y_o,t_o)) \\ &\le V(y_o) \\ &\le b(\|y_o\|) \\ &\le a(\varepsilon) \quad . \end{aligned}$$

Thus

$$a(\|y(t,y_o,t_o)\|) \le a(\varepsilon) \quad ,$$

which implies

$$\|y(t,y_o,t_o)\| \le \varepsilon \quad ,$$

since $a(\cdot)$ is a nondecreasing function. Therefore, the system is uniformly stable. In order to show that the system is uniformly asymptotically stable, one needs to find δ_o such that $\|y_o\| < \delta_o$ and for every given $\varepsilon > 0$ there exists $T(\varepsilon)$ such that $t \ge T(\varepsilon) \Rightarrow \|y(t,y_o,t_o)\| < \varepsilon$. Let $r > 0$, and choose

$$\delta_o = \delta(r) \ ,$$

$$T^*(\varepsilon) = b(\delta_o)/c(\delta(\varepsilon)) \quad ,$$

$$\|y_o\| \le \delta_o \quad .$$

Suppose for

$$t \in [t_o, t_o + T^*] \quad ,$$

$$\|y(t,y_o,t_o)\| > \delta(\varepsilon) \quad .$$

Then, using condition (iii), one obtains

$$c(\|y(t,y_0,t_0)\|) \geq c(\delta(\varepsilon)) \quad ,$$

or

$$\dot{V}(y(t,y_0,t_0)) \leq -c(\delta(\varepsilon)) \quad .$$

On integrating this inequality from t_0 to t, one obtains

$$V(y(t,y_0,t_0)) \leq V(y_0) - c(\delta(\varepsilon))[t-t_0]$$

$$\leq b(\delta_0) - c(\delta(\varepsilon))[t-t_0] \quad ,$$

or

$$V(y(t_0+T^*,y_0,t_0)) \leq b(\delta_0) - c(\delta(\varepsilon))T^* = 0 \quad ,$$

which is a contradiction. Therefore, there exists $t^* \in [t_0,t_0+T^*]$ such that

$$\|y(t^*,y_0,t_0)\| < \delta(\varepsilon) \quad .$$

On choosing $T(\varepsilon) = T^*$, it follows that

$$\|y(t,y(t^*,y_0,t_0),t^*)\| < \varepsilon \quad , \quad \text{for } t \geq t^* \quad ,$$

and therefore the system is uniformly asymptotically stable. On observing that r may be chosen arbitrarily large and $a(r) \to \infty$ as $r \to \infty$, uniform asymptotic stability in the large follows. ◆

In the theorem above, assumptions on the functions V,a,b and c may be relaxed in a variety of ways. For example $c(\cdot)$ does not have to be a non-decreasing function.

Example: The harmonic oscillator is described by

$$\dot{y}_1 = y_2$$

$$\dot{y}_2 = -y_1 \quad . \tag{15}$$

Consider $V(y) = y_1^2 + y_2^2$; then $\dot{V}(y) = 0$. Therefore, the system is stable. A modification of the harmonic oscillator is given by

$$\begin{aligned} \dot{y}_1 &= y_2 - ay_1(y_1^2 + y_2^2) \\ \dot{y}_2 &= -y_1 - ay_2(y_1^2 + y_2^2) \quad . \end{aligned} \tag{16}$$

Consider the same positive definite function; then $\dot{V}(y) = -a(y_1^2 + y_2^2)$, and the system is asymptotically stable in the large provided that $a > 0$.

Example: A damped harmonic oscillator is described by

$$\begin{aligned} \dot{y}_1 &= y_2 \\ \dot{y}_2 &= -y_1 - ay_2 \quad . \end{aligned} \tag{17}$$

Consider the positive definite function $V(y) = y_1^2 + y_2^2$. Then $\dot{V}(y) = -2ay_2^2$ and is negative semidefinite. Therefore, the system is stable. However, on observing the system, one finds that the system is asymptotically stable in the large. This fact is not brought out by the above theorem.

The following result, due to LaSalle [1], is very useful in cases where the derivative of the Liapunov function is negative semidefinite but not negative definite.

LaSalle theorem: Let $V(y)$ be a scalar function with continuous partial derivatives satisfying

(i) $V(y) > 0$ if $y \neq 0$, and $V(0) = 0$,

(ii) $\dot{V}(y) \leq 0$ if $y \neq 0$, and $\dot{V}(0) = 0$,

(iii) $V(y) \to \infty$ as $\|y\| \to \infty$,

(iv) $\dot{V}(y(t,y_0,t_0))$ is not identically zero along

any solution $y(t, y_0, t_0)$ other than the trivial solution $y = 0$.

Then the equilibrium point at the origin for the system (14) is asymptotically stable in the large.

Exercise 9: Apply LaSalle's Theorem to investigate the stability of $\ddot{x} + f(x)\dot{x} + g(x) = 0$ via the Liapunov function $\frac{1}{2}\dot{x}^2 + \int_0^x g(\tau)d\tau$.

It may be observed that the condition that $V(\cdot)$ be radially unbounded, *i.e.*, $V(y) \to \infty$ as $\|y\| \to \infty$, is critical, as illustrated by the following example.

Example: Consider the system

$$\dot{y}_1 = -6y_1/(1 + y_1^2)^2 + 2y_2$$

$$\dot{y}_2 = -2(y_1 + y_2)/(1 + y_1^2)^2 \quad ,$$

with

$$V(y) = y_1^2/(1 + y_1^2) + y_2^2 > 0 \quad \text{if} \quad y \neq 0 \quad ,$$

and, along the solution of the system,

$$\dot{V}(y) = -12y_1^2/(1 + y_1^2)^4 - 4y_2^2/(1 + y_1^2)^2 < 0 \quad \text{if} \quad y \neq 0 \quad .$$

$V(y)$ does not satisfy the conditions of the theorem above, since $V(y)$ does not $\to \infty$ as $y_1 \to \infty$ and $y_2 = 0$.

Exercise 10: Sketch the trajectories for the system

$$\dot{y}_1 = -6y_1/(1 + y_1^2)^2 + 2y_2$$

$$\dot{y}_2 = -2(y_1 + y_2)/(1 + y_1^2)^2 \quad ,$$

and constant-V curves for the positive definite function

$$V(y) = y_1^2/(1 + y_1^2) + y_2^2 \quad .$$

Show the manner in which certain trajectories cross the constant-V curves and escape to infinity.

The importance of the function c(r) for the asymptotic stability of a time-varying system may be seen by considering the system

$$\dot{y} = -e^{-t}y \quad ,$$

and the Liapunov function

$$V(y) = y^2 \quad .$$

Here $\dot{V} = -2y^2 e^{-t} < 0$, but there is no function c(r) such that

$$\dot{V} \leq -c(\|y\|) < 0, \qquad y \neq 0 \quad .$$

It may be noted that the system is stable but not asymptotically stable.

Exercise 11 (Barbashin [1]*):* Show that the system

$$\dot{y}_1 = y_2$$

$$\dot{y}_2 = y_3$$

$$\dot{y}_3 = -f(y_1) - g(y_2) - ay_3$$

is asymptotically stable in the large provided that

(i) f(0) = 0 = g(0) and f, g are differentiable functions,

(ii) $a > 0$,

(iii) $f(y_1)/y_1 \geq \varepsilon_1 > 0$ if $y_1 \neq 0$,

(iv) $ag(y_2)/y_2 - df(y_1)/dy_1 \geq \varepsilon_2 > 0$ if $y_2 \neq 0$.

Use the Liapunov function

$$V(y) = aF(y_1) + f(y_1)y_2 + G(y_2) + (a_2y_2 + y_3)^2/2 ,$$

where

$$F(y_1) \triangleq \int_0^{y_1} f(\tau)d\tau, \quad G(y_2) \triangleq \int_0^{y_2} g(\tau)d\tau .$$

Exercise 12 (Krasovskii [1]): Show that the system

$$\dot{y} = Y(y) \quad ,$$

is asymptotically stable in the large if

$$-F(y) = -\left[\left(\frac{\partial Y}{\partial y}\right) + \left(\frac{\partial Y}{\partial y}\right)'\right] \quad ,$$

is positive definite and

$$V(y) = \sum_{i=1}^{n} Y_i^2(y) \to \infty \text{ as } \|y\| \to \infty .$$

(*Hint:* Use the Liapunov function $V(y)$.)

Exercise 13: Show that the result above by Krasovskii is sufficient but not necessary for the stability of a system by using the second-order system

$$\dot{y} = \begin{bmatrix} a_{11} & a_{12} \\ a_{21} & a_{22} \end{bmatrix} y \quad ,$$

for which the necessary and sufficient conditions for asymptotic stability in the large are known.

Exercise 14 (Infante [1]): Show that the system

$$\dot{y} = A(t)y \quad ,$$

is asymptotically stable if for some positive-definite constant matrix B and some $\varepsilon > 0$,

$$\lim_{t\to\infty} \frac{1}{t-t_o} \int_{t_o}^{t} \lambda_{max}[A'(\tau) + BA(\tau)B^{-1}]d\tau \leq -\varepsilon ,$$

where $\lambda_{max}[A'(\tau)+BA(\tau)B^{-1}]$ represents the maximum eigenvalue of matrix $A'(\tau)+BA(\tau)B^{-1}$.
(*Hint:* Use $y'By$ as the Liapunov function.)

Exercise 15: Investigate the stability of the system

$$\dot{y} = Ay ,$$

using the Liapunov function

$$V(y) = y'Py ,$$

where
$$P \triangleq \int_0^\infty e^{A'\tau}Qe^{A\tau}\,d\tau ,$$

for a given positive definite matrix Q.

The determination of stability via Liapunov's Direct Method centers around the choice of a positive definite function. If the choice is suitable, one is able to deduce the stability of the system. However, there is no universal method for the choice of Liapunov functions. In fact, this is a major drawback of the method. Several techniques have been devised for the choice of Liapunov functions as seen in the exercises above, and each one is applicable to a particular class of systems. However, there are several results on the existence of Liapunov functions. For example, if a system is asymptotically stable, then there exists a Liapunov function satisfying the condition of the theorem on asymptotic stability. The interested reader is referred to Halanay [1]. This knowledge that there exists a Liapunov function if the system is stable does not make the choice of the function any easier.

Sometimes it is possible to show that the system is unstable via the Liapunov method, and there are several results on the instability of systems. An obvious result is: if $V(\cdot)$ and $\dot{V}(\cdot)$ are positive definite, the origin is unstable. The severe condition on $\dot{V}(\cdot)$ may be relaxed to the following:

$$\dot{V}(y) = \lambda V(y) + W(y) \quad , \quad \text{for all } y \quad ,$$

where $\lambda > 0$ and $W(\cdot) \geq 0$ in a neighborhood η of the origin. The conditions for instability have been further relaxed by Četaev [1] to give the following theorem:

Četaev instability theorem: The origin is an unstable equilibrium point if there exists a function $V(y)$, with continuous partial derivatives in a neighborhood η of the origin, and $\eta^* \subset \eta$ such that

(i) the origin is a boundary point of η^*; and $V(y) = 0$, when y is a boundary point of η^*;

(ii) $V(y)$ and $\dot{V}(y) \geq 0$, if $y \in \eta^*$.

5. *Popov Frequency Method*

The system described by

$$\begin{aligned} \dot{x} &= Ax - b\phi(\sigma) \\ \sigma &= c'x \quad , \end{aligned} \tag{17}$$

where A is a constant matrix, b and c are constant vectors and $\phi(\sigma)$ is a continuous function of σ describing the nonlinearity, has been the subject of intensive study by several researchers. The study of this problem was initiated by Lur'e and important results have been obtained recently by Kalman, Popov and several others. The early history of the problem is described by Aizerman and Gantmacher [1].

The following assumptions hold throughout the discussion of this problem:

(i) The eigenvalues of the constant matrix A are in the open left half-plane,

(ii) $\phi(0) = 0$,

(iii) $0 < \phi(\sigma)/\sigma \leq k < \infty, \sigma \neq 0$.

The conditions (ii) and (iii) on the nonlinearity are expressed by saying that $\phi(\cdot)$ is in the sector $(0,k]$. The problem stated above is called "the principal case" by Aizerman and Gantmacher [1] and "the direct control case" by Lefschetz [2]. The system may be reduced to the closed-loop system shown in Figure III-3. $G(s) = c'(sI-A)^{-1}b$, where I is the identity matrix. An essential feature of the problem above is that the nonlinearity is specified by a sector rather than a particular nonlinear function. This is motivated by engineering applications where nonlinear

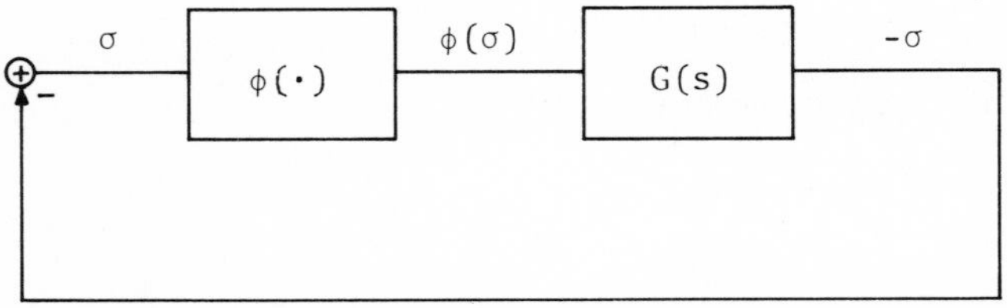

FIGURE III-3: Lur'e system.

characteristics may not be specified precisely, or the nonlinear characteristic may change with time due to aging of the components, or other effects. The concept of stability for every characteristic in a given sector is called "absolute stability." Formally,

Definition: Absolute stability. If the equilibrium point at the origin for the system (17) is asymptotically stable in the large for every $\phi(\cdot)$, such that $0 < \phi(\sigma)/\sigma \leq k$, then the origin is said to be absolutely stable in the sector $(0,k]$.

The following interesting question was posed by Aizerman: "Does the stability of the system (17) for every $\phi(\sigma) = h\sigma$, $k_1 \leq h \leq k_2$, imply the stability of the system for every $\phi(\cdot)$ in the sector $[k_1,k_2]$?" Aizerman conjectured the answer to the question to be "yes;" but it is known now that Aizerman's conjecture is false.

Kalman [2] asked the following similar question: "Does the stability of the system (17) for every $\phi(\sigma) = h\sigma$, $\hat{k}_1 \leq h \leq \hat{k}_2$, imply the stability of nonlinear system (17) in the sector $[k_1,k_2]$ for every $\phi(\cdot)$ such that $\hat{k}_1 \leq \frac{d\phi(\sigma)}{d\sigma} \leq \hat{k}_2$ and $k_1\sigma \leq \phi(\sigma) \leq k_2\sigma$, where $\hat{k}_1 \leq k_1 \leq k_2 \leq \hat{k}_2$?" Kalman has restricted the allowable scope of the nonlinear characteristics more than Aizerman. However, it has been found that the answer to Kalman's question is also "no." In view of these results, essentially two questions may be asked:

(a) Given the parameters A, b, c, is the system (17) absolutely stable?

(b) Given the parameters A, b, c, what is the maximum k so that the system is absolutely stable?

The answer to these questions may be investigated via the use of the Liapunov Function

$$V(x) = x'Px + \beta \int_0^{\sigma} \phi(u)\,du \quad , \qquad (18)$$

where $P = \int_0^{\infty} e^{A'\tau} Q e^{A\tau} d\tau$, Q is a positive definite matrix, and β is a positive constant. It may be observed that P satisfies the matrix equation

$$PA + A'P = -Q \quad , \qquad (19)$$

and is positive definite. Thus, $V(0) = 0$, $V(x) > 0$, $x \neq 0$, and $V(x) \to \infty$ as $\|x\| \to \infty$. Now

$$\dot{V}(x) = -x'Qx - x'(2Pb - \beta A'c)\phi(\sigma) - \beta c'b\phi^2(\sigma) \quad ,$$

and the expression for $\dot{V}(x)$ may be rewritten as

$$\dot{V}(x) = -(\sigma - \frac{\phi(\sigma)}{k})\ \phi(\sigma) - [x',\phi]\tilde{Q}\begin{bmatrix} x \\ \phi \end{bmatrix} \quad ,$$

where

$$\tilde{Q} = \begin{bmatrix} Q & -\alpha \\ -\alpha' & \gamma \end{bmatrix}$$

$$\alpha = Pb - \frac{\beta A'c + c}{2}$$

$$\gamma = \beta c'b + 1/k \quad .$$

If $\tilde{Q}$ is positive definite, then $\dot{V}$ is negative definite, and the condition for positive definiteness of $\tilde{Q}$ reduces to the inequality

$$\gamma - \alpha' Q^{-1}\alpha > 0 \quad ,$$

or

$$1/k > \alpha' Q^{-1}\alpha - \beta c'b \quad .$$

It is seen from the above inequality that the value k, *i.e.*, the sector of stability, depends in general on the choice of β and Q.

Example: Consider the system

$$\dot{x}_1 = x_2$$

$$\dot{x}_2 = -x_1 - x_2 - \phi(-x_1 + x_2) ,$$

and the Liapunov function

$$V(x_1,x_2) = [x_1\ x_2] \begin{bmatrix} 3/2 & 1/2 \\ 1/2 & 1 \end{bmatrix} \begin{bmatrix} x_1 \\ x_2 \end{bmatrix} + \frac{1}{2} \int_0^{-x_1+x_2} \phi(u)\,du .$$

Then the inequality for the sector is

$$k < \frac{16}{33} .$$

Exercise 16: Find the conditions for the asymptotic stability in the large of the system

$$\dot{x}_1 = x_2$$

$$\dot{x}_2 = -f(\sigma) ,$$

where $\sigma = a_0x_1 + a_1x_2$ and $a_0, a_1 > 0$, via the Liapunov function

$$V = \frac{1}{2} a_1 x_2^2 + \int_0^{\sigma} f(u)\,du .$$

(*Careful!* $\frac{1}{2} a_1x_2^2$ is not a positive definite function of x_1 and x_2.)

Exercise 17: (Asner [1]) Find the conditions for the asymptotic stability in the large of the system

$$\dot{x}_1 = x_2$$

$$\dot{x}_2 = x_3$$

$$\dot{x}_3 = -f(\sigma) \quad ,$$

where $\sigma = a_0x_1 + a_1x_2 + a_2x_3$, and $a_0,a_1,a_2 > 0$, via the Liapunov function

$$V = \frac{1}{2} x' \, Gx + \int_0^\sigma h(u) \, du \quad .$$

Here

$$G = \frac{a_0^2}{a_1a_2} \begin{bmatrix} a_0 & a_1 & 0 \\ a_1 & a_2^2 + \frac{a_1^2}{a_0} & \frac{a_1a_2}{a_0} \\ 0 & \frac{a_1a_2}{a_0} & \frac{a_1^2a_2}{a_0} \end{bmatrix}$$

$$h(\sigma) = f(\sigma) - \frac{a_0}{a_1a_2} \sigma \, .$$

(*Careful!* Determinant of $G \equiv 0$. *Hint:* Use LaSalle's Theorem.)

More recently, the problem above has been approached by Popov [1] in the frequency domain. The main result may be stated as follows:

Popov theorem: The system (17) is absolutely stable in the sector $(0,k]$ if there is a real number q such that the inequality

$$\mathrm{Re}\{(1 + j\omega q) \, G(j\omega)\} + 1/k \geq \eta > 0 \quad , \tag{20}$$

holds for all real $\omega \geq 0$, where η is an arbitrarily small number.

It should be emphasized that in the statement of the theorem above, $0 < k < \infty$. Equation (20) involves checking the positiveness of a function on the $j\omega$ axis, also known as the frequency axis. This consequently leads to the connotation of "frequency-type" or "frequency-domain" criterion for relations such as (20). The proof of the Popov theorem is beyond the scope of the present notes and is omitted here. It can be found in Hsu and Meyer [1].

It is interesting to begin the discussion of the Popov theorem by considering the linear case $\phi(\sigma) = h\sigma$ and the application of the Nyquist criterion to this linear system. Let

$$X_N = \text{Re}\{G(j\omega)\}$$

$$Y_N = \text{Im}\{G(j\omega)\}$$

$$W_N = X_N + j\,Y_N \quad .$$

Then, the linear system with $\phi(\sigma) = h\sigma$, is stable provided that the plot of W_N in the (X_N, Y_N)-plane does not encircle the point $(-1/h, 0)$, as shown in Figure III-4. For details of Nyquist criterion, see Elgerd [1].

The "Popov inequality" (20) has an elegant geometrical interpretation similar to the Nyquist criterion. By letting

$$X_p = \text{Re}\{G(j\omega)\}$$

$$Y_p = \omega\,\text{Im}\{G(j\omega)\}$$

$$W_p = X_p + j\,Y_p \quad ,$$

the inequality (20) becomes

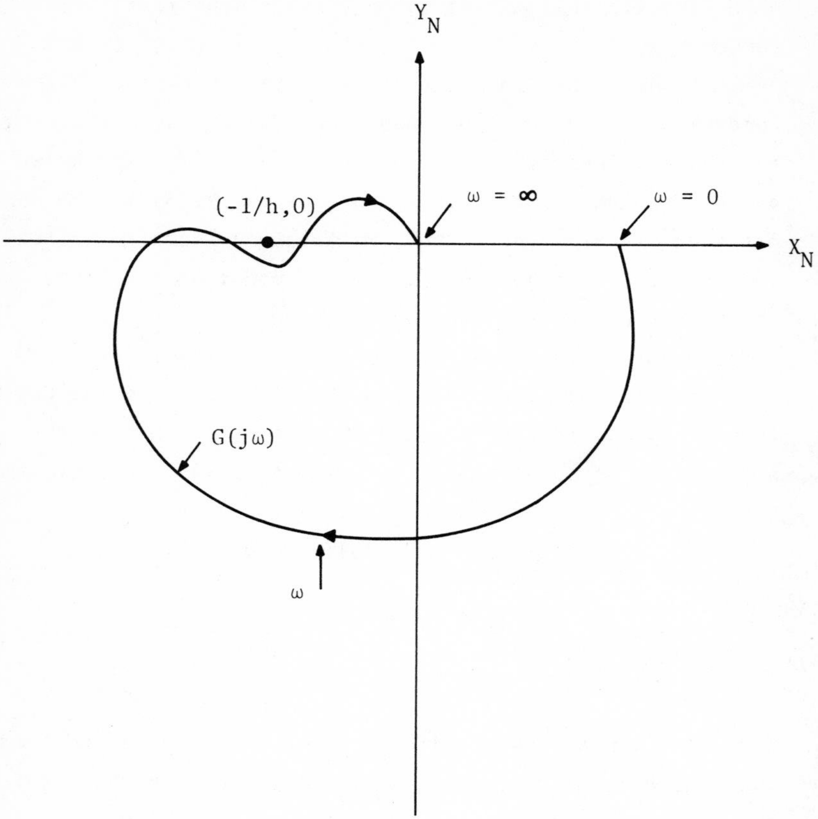

FIGURE III-4: Nyquist plot.

$$X_p - q\,Y_p + 1/k \geq \eta > 0. \tag{21}$$

The satisfaction of the equality $X_p - q\,Y_p + 1/k = 0$ in the (X_p, Y_p)-plane involves the finding of a straight line, the so-called Popov line, with slope $1/q$, intersecting the X_p-axis at $-1/k$. That is, for stability, the plot of W_p, with

ω as a parameter, lies strictly to the right of the Popov line. Or, in other words, the closed half-plane to the left of the Popov line is the "forbidden region." This is illustrated in Figure III-5.

It is seen from the Popov and Nyquist diagrams that the Popov diagram is obtained by a distortion of the Nyquist diagram, *i.e.*, by multiplying the imaginary part, Im{G(jω)},

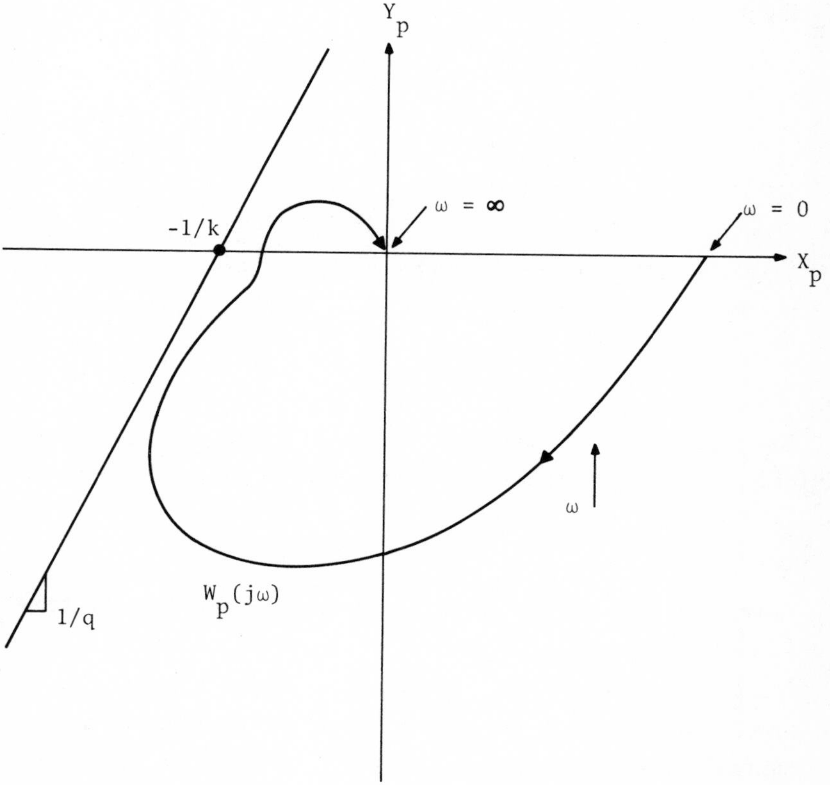

FIGURE III-5: Popov plot.

by ω. Two observations may be made concerning the two criteria: (i) the Hurwitz sector (*i.e.*, the sector for which the linear system is stable) is always bigger than or equal to the Popov sector (*i.e.*, the sector for which the nonlinear system is absolutely stable); (ii) the Nyquist condition is necessary and sufficient, whereas the Popov condition is only sufficient for stability.

Example: Consider the following linear system, corresponding to Exercise 17 of this chapter:

$$\dot{x}_1 = x_2$$

$$\dot{x}_2 = x_3$$

$$\dot{x}_3 = -k_h(a_0x_1 + a_1x_2 + a_2x_3) \quad .$$

A simple application of Routh-Hurwitz criterion yields that the system is asymptotically stable in the large provided

$$k_h > a_0/a_1a_2 \quad .$$

The application of LaSalle's Theorem to the system of Exercise 17 yields that the nonlinear system is stable provided

$$f(\sigma)/\sigma > a_0/a_1a_2 \quad .$$

Thus, the sectors for which the linear system and the nonlinear system are asymptotically stable in the large are identical in this case. Let us apply Popov's result to the problem of Exercise 17. The problem may be reduced to the suitable form by defining

$$f(\sigma) = k\sigma + \phi(\sigma) \quad .$$

Then the linear part is given by

$$G(s) = \frac{a_2 s^2 + a_1 s + a_0}{s^3 + k(a_2 s^2 + a_1 s + a_0)} .$$

The eigenvalues of the linear part are in the open left half-plane provided

$$k > a_0/a_1 a_2 .$$

The Popov inequality for q = 0 becomes

$$k|N(j\omega)|^2 + \mathrm{Re}\{N(j\omega)\ (-j\omega)^3\} \geq \eta > 0 , \quad (22)$$

where

$$N(j\omega) = (a_0 - a_2\ \omega^2) + j\ a_1\ \omega .$$

A sufficient condition for the satisfaction of the inequality (22) is given by

$$k > a_1/a_2^2 \quad \text{and} \quad a_1^2 - 2a_0 a_2 > 0 .$$

It is easily seen that this condition is more restrictive than the earlier condition $k_h > a_0/a_1 a_2$. Thus, in general, for a given value of q, (20) will yield sufficient conditions for the stability of the system.

Exercise 18: For the system of Figure III-3, where $G(s) = 1/(s+1)^n$, n is odd > 3, the Nyquist plot and Popov plot are similar and are nearly the same. Determine if the Hurwitz sector and the Popov sectors are the same.

Exercise 19: Discuss the stability of the system

$$\dot{x}_1 = x_2 \qquad \dot{x}_3 = x_4$$

$$\dot{x}_2 = x_3 \qquad \dot{x}_4 = -f(\sigma) ,$$

where $\sigma = a_0x_1 + a_1x_2 + a_2x_3 + a_3x_4$, and $a_0, a_1, a_2, a_3 > 0$.

Exercise 20: (Jackson and Aggarwal [1]) Discuss the stability of the system

$$x^{(n)} + \rho_n + f(\sigma_n) = 0 \quad ,$$

where

$$\sigma_n = a_{n-1}x^{(n-1)} + a_{n-2}x^{(n-2)} + \ldots + a_1\dot{x} + a_0x$$

$$\rho_n = b_{n-1}x^{(n-1)} + b_{n-2}x^{(n-2)} + \ldots + b_1\dot{x} + b_0x \quad ,$$

where the superscripts on x represent the order of the time derivatives.

Exercise 21: For the system of Figure III-3 find the Hurwitz and Popov sectors, where the linear part is given by

(i) $$G(s) = \frac{s + 1.5}{(s+1)(s+2)}$$

(ii) $$G(s) = \frac{(s+1.5)(s+2.5)}{(s+1)(s+2)(s+3)}$$

(iii) $$G(s) = \frac{1}{(s+2)^3}$$

(iv) $$G(s) = \frac{1}{((s+\alpha)^2 + \beta^2)(s+1)} \quad , \alpha, \beta > 0 \quad .$$

To bridge the gap between the necessary and sufficient Nyquist condition for linear systems and the sufficient (but not necessary) Popov condition for nonlinear systems of the form (17), it is only natural to look for improved results by formulating the problem more precisely. For example, if the nonlinear characteristic $\phi(\cdot)$ is known to lie in a $[\underline{k},k]$ sector, $k \geq \underline{k} > 0$, instead of a $(0,k]$ sector, a frequency criterion of similar form as (20) can be obtained. Again, if bounds on the derivatives of $\phi(\cdot)$ are known another complicated frequency-type criterion, similar to (20) can be obtained. Furthermore, for different types of nonlinearities $\phi(\cdot)$, say a pulsed modulator, Popov-type results could also be obtained. References to results of this type can be found in Zames [1], Hsu and Meyer [1], Dewey [1], Jury and Lee [1], Kan and Jury [1], Bergen and Sapiro [1] and Bergen, Iwens, and Rault [1].

To conclude, it should be mentioned that in the stability study of nonlinear systems, there have been only two* successful approaches, namely the Liapunov method and the Popov method. Moreover, it has been shown (*e.g.*, Kalman [3], Jakubovič [1], Baker and Bergen [1]) that under certain restrictions these two methods are equivalent. However, from practical experience it is known that the Popov approach, *i.e.*, the frequency-type criterion, is much simpler and more easily applicable as a design tool than the Liapunov method. The excellent survey paper by Brockett [1] is recommended to the reader for further study of the subject of stability.

---

* In recent years functional-analysis techniques have been successfully exploited to derive some "Small Gain"-type stability results. These techniques require a higher level of mathematics before they can be appropriately introduced; thus, they are omitted here.

CHAPTER IV

LIMIT CYCLES AND AMPLITUDE BOUNDS

1. *Limit Cycles*

The differential equation

$$\ddot{x} + x = 0 \tag{1}$$

describes one of the simplest forms of periodic motion. The solution of the differential equation is given by A sin(t+ϕ), where A and ϕ are determined by initial conditions. The equation of motion for this simple harmonic motion may be written as

$$\begin{aligned} \dot{x}_1 &= x_2 \\ \dot{x}_2 &= -x_1 \quad , \end{aligned} \tag{2}$$

and the trajectories in the phase plane consist of closed circles as shown in Figure IV-1. Each circle in the phase plane corresponds to a periodic solution and the initial conditions determine the circle. Two important observations may be made: (i) every initial condition gives rise to a periodic solution, and (ii) there is a continuum of periodic solutions.

A periodic behavior quite distinct from the above is observed in certain nonlinear systems. Consider the system

$$\begin{aligned} \dot{x}_1 &= x_2 + x_1(x_1^2+x_2^2)^{-1/2}(1-x_1^2-x_2^2) \\ \dot{x}_2 &= -x_1 + x_2(x_1^2+x_2^2)^{-1/2}(1-x_1^2-x_2^2) \quad . \end{aligned} \tag{3}$$

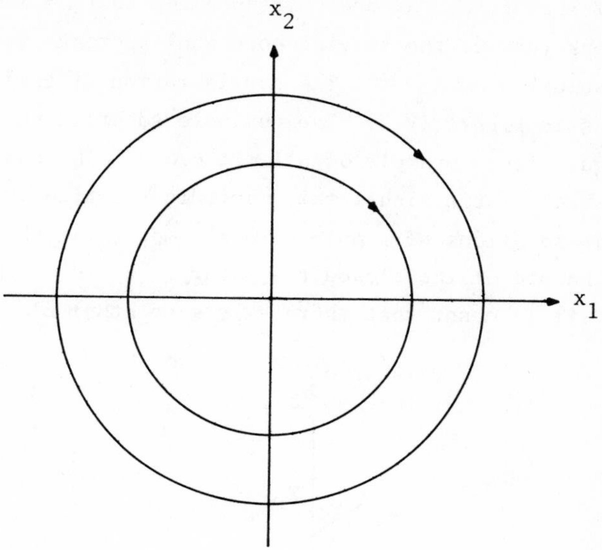

FIGURE IV-1: Trajectories of simple harmonic motion.

This system, in polar coordinates, is given by

$$\dot{r} = 1 - r^2$$

$$\dot{\theta} = -1 ,$$

and the solution is given by

$$r(t) = (Ae^{2t} - 1)/(Ae^{2t} + 1)$$

$$\theta(t) = \theta_o - t ,$$

where

$$A \triangleq (1+r_o)/(1-r_o), \quad r_o \neq 1 .$$

When $r_o = 1$, $r(t) \equiv 1$ and $\theta(t) = \theta_o - t$. There is only one periodic solution, the one corresponding to $r_o = 1$ and all solutions (except the trivial solution) approach the periodic solution as $t \to \infty$. The configuration of trajectories is shown in Figure IV-2. The periodic solution shown in the figure is an example of a limit cycle. The basic property which distinguishes this periodic solution from the periodic solutions of simple harmonic motion is the "isolated" nature of the closed trajectory. By the term "isolated," it is meant that there exists no other closed tra-

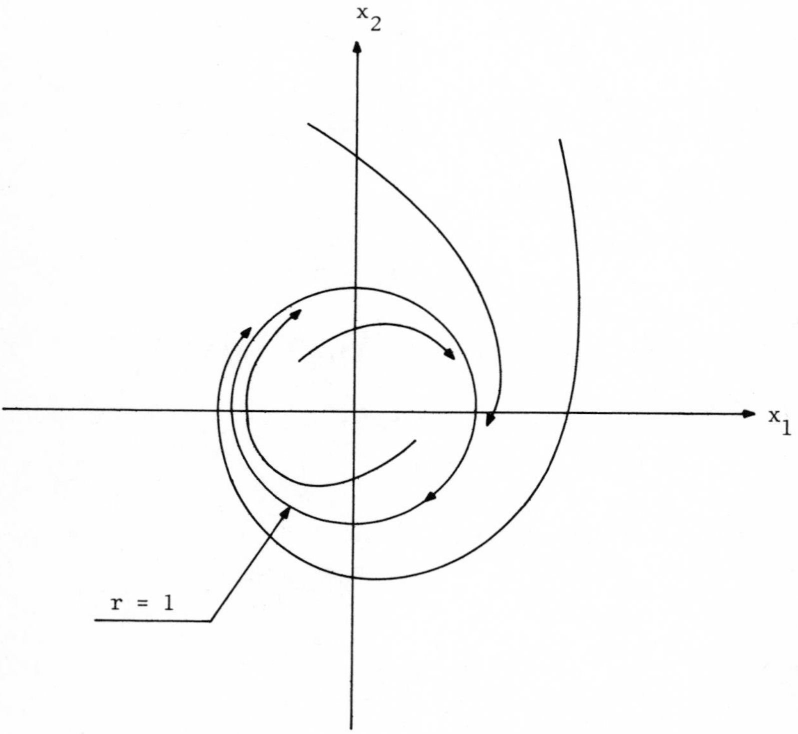

FIGURE IV-2: Limit cycle.

jectory in a sufficiently small neighborhood of the particular trajectory called the limit cycle. Needless to add, limit cycles do not exist in linear systems.

Definition: Limit cycle. A limit cycle is a closed trajectory which does not belong to a continuous family of closed trajectories, *i.e.*, an isolated closed trajectory.

The above example of a limit cycle is a contrived one, and is used to illustrate clearly the concept of an isolated periodic solution. One of the earliest examples of physical systems exhibiting a limit cycle was discovered by van der Pol [1]. The physical system was modeled by

$$\ddot{x}_1 + \varepsilon\, \dot{x}_1(x_1^2-1) + x_1 = 0$$

or

$$\begin{aligned} \dot{x}_1 &= x_2 \\ \dot{x}_2 &= -\varepsilon\, x_2(x_1^2-1) - x_1 \quad , \end{aligned} \tag{4}$$

where $\varepsilon > 0$, and is known as van der Pol's system. In this case, an explicit closed-form solution is not possible, and it requires a certain amount of sophisticated analysis to show the existence of a unique periodic solution. One of the objectives of this chapter is to develop these techniques of analysis. Higher-order systems also exhibit limit cycles. For example, the third-order system

$$\begin{aligned} \dot{x}_1 &= x_1 + x_2 - x_1(x_1^2 + x_2^2) \\ \dot{x}_2 &= -x_1 + x_2 - x_2(x_1^2 + x_2^2) \\ \dot{x}_3 &= -x_3 \end{aligned} \tag{5}$$

considered by Zubov [1], is shown to have a limit cycle. A more interesting and still-unsolved problem is the problem of limit cycles for the system described by

$$
\begin{aligned}
\dot{x}_1 &= x_2 \\
\dot{x}_2 &= -\varepsilon_1 x_2(x_1^2 - 1) - x_1 - c(x_1-x_3) \\
\dot{x}_3 &= x_4 \\
\dot{x}_4 &= -\varepsilon_2 x_4(x_3^2 - 1) - x_3 + c(x_1-x_3) \quad ,
\end{aligned} \tag{6}
$$

where ε_1, ε_2 and c are positive constants. In this case of two coupled van der Pol oscillators, "periodic" solutions have been observed when the differential equations are solved numerically on the computer. However, up to the present time, it has not been shown analytically whether the numerically observed solutions are indeed periodic solutions.

In the above examples, limit cycles are "stable." All trajectories (except the trivial solution) approach the one limit-cycle trajectory. In general, there may be several limit cycles, and trajectories may tend away from a limit cycle, thus giving rise to "unstable" limit cycles. In the following, attention will be devoted to stable limit cycles; however, similar concepts hold for unstable limit cycles.

Analytical results are available for finding limit cycles in second-order systems. However, there are few results for higher-order systems. Failing to find periodic solutions, researchers have turned their attention to obtaining regions in the state space which ultimately contain the trajectory. Various results useful in the determination of periodic solutions or the ultimate behavior of solutions are presented in this chapter.

2. *Index*

A useful concept in the consideration of the periodic solutions of second-order systems is the notion of a vector field in a plane. A vector field F in the (x_1,x_2)-plane is given by associating with each point (x_1,x_2) in the (x_1,x_2)-plane an ordered pair (F_1,F_2). F_1 and F_2 depend upon the point (x_1,x_2) and define, respectively, the x_1 and x_2 components of a vector at the point (x_1,x_2). Consider again the system

$$\begin{aligned} \dot{x}_1 &= X_1(x_1,x_2) \\ \dot{x}_2 &= X_2(x_1,x_2) \quad , \end{aligned} \tag{7}$$

and define a vector field F in the (x_1,x_2)-plane associated with this differential system. Let the x_1-component of this vector field be $X_1(x_1,x_2)$ and the x_2-component of the vector field be $X_2(x_1,x_2)$. Thus, the vector field is defined for every point of the phase plane; *i.e.*, a direction as well as magnitude of the vector is given (except at the singular points). The magnitude is given by the length of the vector and the direction is signified by placing an arrow on the vector. The direction of the vector is tangent to the trajectory passing through the point in the phase plane. At a singular point, the magnitude of the vector is zero, and the direction of the trajectory is not defined.

Let a simple closed rectifiable positively oriented curve C be given in the (x_1,x_2)-plane. The name "scroc" is assigned to such curves (see Hille [1]). The term *positively oriented* is used to signify that the curve is oriented in the counter-clockwise direction.

A scroc C and a vector field $F = (X_1(x_1,x_2),X_2(x_1,x_2))$ in the (x_1,x_2)-plane are related by the assignment of a number called the "index" of the scroc relative to the vector field. The index is a measure of the change in direction of the vector field around the closed curve. This change is meaningful only if there is no singular point of the system on the scroc.

Definition: Index. The index of a scroc C with respect to the vector field $F = (X_1(x_1,x_2),\ X_2(x_1,x_2))$ is defined as

$$\frac{1}{2\pi}\oint_C d\left(\tan^{-1}\frac{X_2(x_1,x_2)}{X_1(x_1,x_2)}\right) = \frac{1}{2\pi}\oint_C \frac{X_1 dX_2 - X_2 dX_1}{X_1^2 + X_2^2},$$

provided there are no singular points of the system on the scroc C. The index of an isolated singular point P in the phase plane is the same as the index of a scroc C such that

(i) P is an interior point of the scroc C

(ii) the scroc C contains no other singular points in its interior.

It must be emphasized that the contour integral is taken in the counter-clockwise direction and there are no singular points on the scroc.

For the linear system,

$$\begin{aligned} \dot{z}_1 &= a_{11}z_1 + a_{12}\,z_2 \\ \dot{z}_2 &= a_{21}z_1 + a_{22}\,z_2\,, \end{aligned} \tag{8}$$

the index of the isolated singularity at the origin may be evaluated by considering the scroc C, which is a circle of radius r_o. Parameterizing,

$$z_1 = r_o \cos\theta$$

and

$$z_2 = r_o \sin\theta\ ,$$

the expression for the index in this case reduces to

$$\frac{a_{11}a_{22}-a_{12}a_{21}}{2\pi}\int_0^{2\pi}[\cos^2\theta(a_{11}^2+a_{21}^2)+\sin^2\theta(a_{12}^2+a_{22}^2)$$

$$+\,2\sin\theta\cos\theta(a_{11}a_{12}+a_{21}a_{22})]^{-1}\,d\theta$$

$$=(a_{11}a_{22}-a_{12}a_{21})/|a_{11}a_{22}-a_{12}a_{21}|\ .$$

Observing that the eigenvalues are given by the characteristic equation

$$\lambda^2-(a_{11}+a_{22})\lambda+(a_{11}a_{22}-a_{12}a_{21})=0\ ,$$

it follows that the index for a saddle is -1. For a focus, a node, or a center, the index is 1. It is also seen that the expression for the index is independent of r_o. This follows from the simple observation that the index of a scroc C which contains no singular points on it or in its interior is zero. Two important results concerning the index are given by the following exercises.

Exercise 1: Let C be a scroc which contains the singular points $s_1,s_2,\ldots,s_k$ of the vector field F in its interior and no singular point on C. Then

$$\text{Index of C}=\sum_{i=1}^{k}\text{Index of } s_i\ .$$

Exercise 2: Let C be a scroc and F_1 and F_2 be vector fields such that

(i) F_1 and F_2 are never in opposition on C

(ii) F_1 and F_2 have no singular point on C.

Show that

the index of C with respect to F_1

= the index of C with respect to F_2 .

By the term *in opposition* it is meant that the arrows indicating the direction of vectors corresponding to the fields F_1 and F_2 point in opposite directions.

Theorem: The index of the singularity at the origin for the system

$$\begin{aligned} \dot{y}_1 &= a_{11}y_1 + a_{12}y_2 + Y_1^*(y_1,y_2) \\ \dot{y}_2 &= a_{21}y_1 + a_{22}y_2 + Y_2^*(y_1,y_2) \end{aligned} \tag{9}$$

$$\begin{aligned} Y_1^* &= O(y_1^2 + y_2^2) \\ Y_2^* &= O(y_1^2 + y_2^2) \end{aligned} \tag{10}$$

and the index of the singularity at the origin for the system

$$\begin{aligned} \dot{z}_1 &= a_{11}z_1 + a_{12}z_2 \\ \dot{z}_2 &= a_{21}z_1 + a_{22}z_2 \end{aligned} \tag{11}$$

are the same provided that $a_{11}a_{22} - a_{12}a_{21} \neq 0$.

Proof: Let the nonlinear system and the linear system define the vector fields F_N and F_L respectively, and consider the index of a circle of radius of r_o relative to these vector fields. If the vector fields are never in opposition on C, then, by Exercise 2, the scroc C has the same index relative to the two vector fields. The components of the two vector fields at a point (z_1,z_2) of the phase plane are:

$$\begin{aligned} F_N&: \ (a_{11}z_1+a_{12}z_2+Y_1^*(z_1,z_2),\ a_{21}z_1+a_{22}z_2+Y_2^*(z_1,z_2)) \\ F_L&: \ (a_{11}z_1+a_{12}z_2,\ a_{21}z_1+a_{22}z_2) \ , \end{aligned} \tag{12}$$

and they are in opposition provided that

$$(1 + \eta^2)\{(a_{11}z_1 + a_{12}z_2)^2 + (a_{21}z_1 + a_{22}z_2)^2\} = \eta^2(Y_1^{*2}(z_1,z_2) + Y_2^{*2}(z_1,z_2)) \tag{13}$$

for some $\eta > 0$. On converting to polar coordinates, this relation on the scroc C reduces to

$$(1+\eta^2)\{(a_{11}\cos\theta + a_{12}\sin\theta)^2 + (a_{21}\cos\theta + a_{22}\sin\theta)^2\} = \eta^2\{O(r_o^2)\}\ . \tag{14}$$

The right-hand side of (14) tends to zero as $r_o \to 0$, independent of θ, whereas the left-hand side, being a continuous function of θ, attains its minimum $\neq 0$ for $r_o \neq 0$ at some $\theta = \hat{\theta}$, $0 \leq \hat{\theta} \leq 2\pi$. Therefore, the equality (14) does not hold for sufficiently small r_o so the two vector fields are never in opposition; hence the theorem. ◆

An important consequence of the results above is given by the following observation. The index of a closed trajectory relative to its own vector field is unity, independent of the number of singular points enclosed by the trajectory. The fact that the vector field is tangential to the scroc makes the observation intuitively clear.

Exercise 3: Show that a periodic solution in the (x_1,x_2)-plane must enclose at least one singular point. Also, show that if there are several isolated singular points enclosed by the periodic solution in the phase plane, then the sum of their indices must be +1.

Exercise 4: Show that a periodic solution cannot enclose a saddle point alone.

Exercise 5: Find the indices of the various periodic solutions of Exercise 9 in Chapter II by summing the indices of the singular points enclosed by the periodic solution.

3. *Existence of Limit Cycles*

There are two results which may be used in the investigation of limit cycles for second-order nonlinear systems, given by Poincaré [1] and Bendixson [1].

Bendixson theorem: A simply connected region R in the phase plane, where the expression

$$\frac{\partial X_1}{\partial x_1} + \frac{\partial X_2}{\partial x_2} \neq 0 \tag{15}$$

does not change sign, contains no closed trajectories.

Proof: Let the vector field defined in Section 2 be denoted by $\underline{X}(x_1,x_2) = \begin{bmatrix} X_1(x_1,x_2) \\ X_2(x_1,x_2) \end{bmatrix}$. Consider a scroc C; then, by the divergence theorem (see Pipes [1], Kaplan [1]) in two dimensions,

$$\begin{aligned} \iint_S \operatorname{div} \underline{X}\, dS &= \iint_S \left(\frac{\partial X_1}{\partial x_1} + \frac{\partial X_2}{\partial x_2} \right) dx_1 dx_2 \\ &= \oint_C \underline{X} \cdot \hat{\underline{n}}\, d\hat{r} \ , \end{aligned} \tag{16}$$

where

$\hat{\underline{n}}$ is the unit vector normal to an element dr of the scroc C and dS is the element of area.

(Figure IV-3 shows the various quantities.) Suppose the

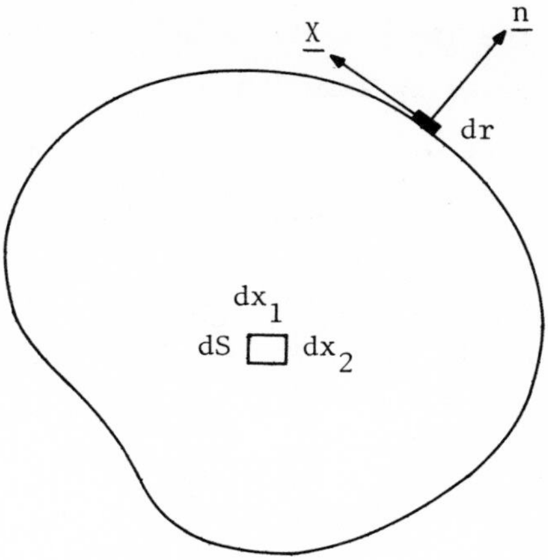

FIGURE IV-3: Vector field and limit cycle.

the scroc C is a closed trajectory corresponding to a periodic solution. Then the vector field is tangential to the curve C and $\underline{X} \cdot \hat{\underline{n}} = 0$ along the curve C. Therefore, the integral

$$\iint_S \left(\frac{\partial X_1}{\partial x_1} + \frac{\partial X_2}{\partial x_2}\right) dx_1 dx_2 = 0 ,$$

and this is possible only if

$$\frac{\partial X_1}{\partial x_1} + \frac{\partial X_2}{\partial x_2}$$

changes sign in the interior of the curve C. Hence a necessary but not sufficient condition for the existence of a closed trajectory in a simply connected region R is that the expression $\frac{\partial X_1}{\partial x_1} + \frac{\partial X_2}{\partial x_2}$ changes sign in R.◆

Bendixson's theorem gives negative information, *i.e.*, the regions where the limit cycle is not located, as illustrated by the following examples.

Example: For the system

$$\begin{aligned} \dot{x}_1 &= -x_2 - x_1(x_1^2 + x_2^2 - 1) \\ \dot{x}_2 &= x_1 - x_2(x_1^2 + x_2^2 - 1) \quad , \end{aligned} \tag{17}$$

the expression

$$\frac{\partial X_1}{\partial x_1} + \frac{\partial X_2}{\partial x_2} = -4(x_1^2 + x_2^2 - 1/2)$$

does not change sign for $(x_1^2 + x_2^2)^{1/2} < 1/\sqrt{2}$. Therefore, no limit cycle exists for $(x_1^2 + x_2^2)^{1/2} < 1/\sqrt{2}$; however, by converting to polar coordinates, it is easily seen that $r = 1$ is a limit cycle.

Example: For the van der Pol equation, the expression $\partial X_1/\partial x_1 + \partial X_2/\partial x_2$ is given by $-\varepsilon(x_1^2 - 1)$. In the region $|x_1| < 1$, this expression does not change sign, and therefore there is no periodic solution lying entirely in the strip. It will be seen later that there is a unique periodic solution which, of course, does not lie entirely in the strip $|x_1| < 1$.

In the following, the Poincaré-Bendixson theorem is presented which gives the region where a limit cycle may be located. The concept of "limit set" is needed for the statement of the theorem, and is defined in the following.

Definition: Limit set of a trajectory. Let $P(t)$ denote the solution point $(x_1(t,x_{1o},x_{2o},t_o),x_2(t,x_{1o},x_{2o},t_o))$ at time t along the trajectory which passes through (x_{1o},x_{2o}) at time t_o; and let L^+ denote the portion of the trajectory for $t_o \leq t < \infty$, called the half trajectory. A point Q is called a limit point of the half trajectory L^+ if there exists a sequence $\{t_n\}$ such that $\lim_{n \to \infty} t_n \to \infty$ and $P(t_n) \to Q$ as $n \to \infty$. The set of limit points of L^+ is denoted by L_e^+.

Example: For the system (3), P(t) is given by $(r(t) \cos \theta(t), r(t) \sin \theta(t))$. Let the sequence $\{t_n\}$ be $\{2\pi n\}$, then the limit point Q is $(\cos \theta_o, \sin \theta_o)$. The set of limit points L_e^+ is the unit circle.

Poincaré-Bendixson theorem: If L^+ is contained in a closed bounded region R, and R contains no singular point, then either L^+ is a periodic solution or L_e^+ is a periodic solution.

The requirements of the theorem are shown pictorially in Figure IV-4. R is a closed and bounded annular region containing no singular point. Let us assume that trajec-

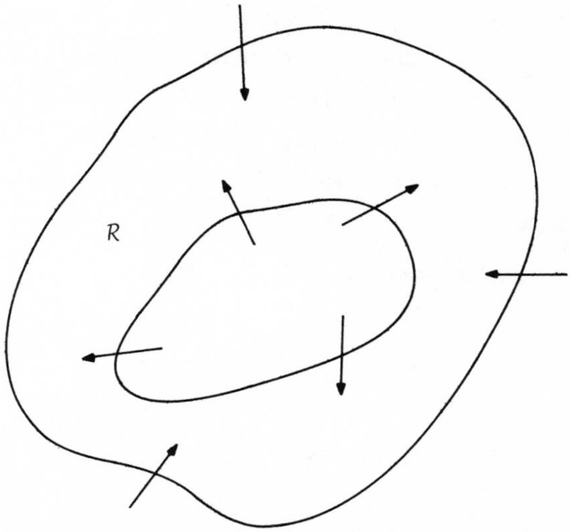

FIGURE IV-4: Region containing limit cycles.

tories are crossing into the annular region at every point of the boundary. Then a trajectory crossing into the annular region will never leave the region R. The conditions of the Poincaré-Bendixson Theorem hold and the region R contains a periodic solution. The proof of this result, omitted here, is found in Coddington and Levinson [1].

There is a difficulty encountered in the application of the Poincaré-Bendixson theorem, and this will be illustrated by the following two examples.

Example: In the case of van der Pol's equation,

$$\begin{aligned} \dot{x}_1 &= x_2 \\ \dot{x}_2 &= -\varepsilon x_2(x_1^2 - 1) - x_1, \ \varepsilon \ll 1, \end{aligned} \tag{18}$$

it is known that there is a periodic solution which does not differ very much from a circle of radius $r = 2$. If one attempts to construct a region R with circles of radii $2 + \eta_1$ and $2 - \eta_2$, $\eta_1, \eta_2 > 0$ and $\eta_2 < 2$, one easily finds that this region R does not contain the trajectories in a manner required by the Poincaré-Bendixson theorem. The actual shape of the region is very important, and in most cases of practical interest, the finding of region R is a difficult task.

Example: For the system (17),

$$\frac{dr}{dt} = (1 - r^2)r \quad , \tag{19}$$

$$\frac{dr}{dt} < 0 \text{ for } r \geq 1 + \eta_1,\ \eta_1 > 0; \text{ and } \frac{dr}{dt} > 0 \text{ for } r < 1 - \eta_2 < 1.$$

The annular region formed by circles of radii $1 - \eta_2$ and $1 + \eta_1$ satisfies the requirements of the Poincaré-Bendixson theorem, and therefore there exists a periodic solution. The annular region and the periodic solution are shown in Figure IV-5.

Several researchers have considered the Liénard equation

$$\begin{aligned} \dot{x}_1 &= x_2 \\ \dot{x}_2 &= -x_2\, f(x_1,x_2) - g(x_1) \end{aligned} \tag{20}$$

with a view to finding a region R in the phase plane which meets the requirements of the Poincaré-Bendixson theorem. Many results have been obtained depending upon the assumptions made upon the nonlinearities f and g. In the following, three of these results are presented as exercises.

Exercise 6: (Levinson [1]) Show that the system (20) has at least one periodic solution provided that there

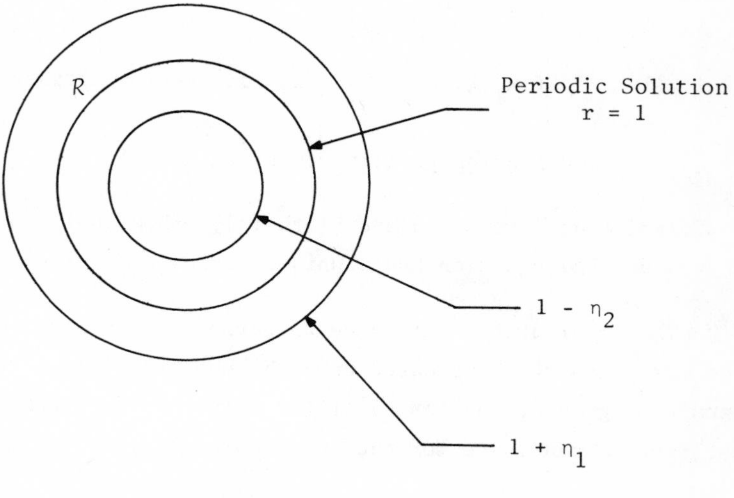

FIGURE IV-5: Region containing the limit cycle for the system (19).

exist positive constants a, m, M such that

(i) $f(x_1,x_2) > m$ if $|x_1| \geq a$, $|x_2| > a$,

(ii) $f(0,0) < 0$; $f(x_1,x_2) > -M$ for all x_1,x_2 ,

(iii) $g(0) = 0$; $x_1 g(x_1) > 0$, $x_1 \neq 0$; $|g(x_1)| \to \infty$,

and $g(x_1) \Big/ \int_0^{x_1} g(u)\,du \to 0$ as $|x_1| \to \infty$.

Exercise 7: (Levinson and Smith [1]) Show that the system (20) has at least one periodic solution, provided that there exist positive constants a, b, M, with $a < b$ such that

(i) $f(x_1,x_2) \geq 0$ if $|x_1| \geq a$ for every x_2,

(ii) as in Exercise 6,

(iii) $g(0) = 0$; $x_1 g(x_1) > 0$, $x_1 \neq 0$, $\int_0^{x_1} g(u)\,du \to \infty$ as $|x_1| \to \infty$,

(iv) $\int_a^b f(x_1,x_2)\,dx_1 > 10\,Ma$ for every arbitrary decreasing positive function $x_2(x_1)$.

Exercise 8: (Levinson and Smith [1]) Show that the van der Pol equation has a unique periodic solution.

The proof of the existence of periodic solution in the exercises above is based upon the construction of the annular region *R*, consisting of two curves as described earlier. A candidate for the inner curve is

$$\lambda(x_1,x_2) = \frac{1}{2} x_2^2 + G(x_1) = \text{constant}$$

where $G(x_1) = \int_0^{x_1} g(u)\,du$. The trajectories of the system cross the curve $\lambda(x_1,x_2) = c$, $c > 0$ sufficiently small, from the interior to the exterior. The nature of the second curve which is crossed from the exterior to the interior by the trajectories is more complicated. The curve is constructed by the detailed consideration of the direction of trajectories in various regions of the phase space. The curve consists of piecewise differentiable arcs. A discussion of the subject of construction of such arcs is found in Cesari [1].

The results above and some modifications of these results are the only results available for the existence of periodic solutions for second-order systems. A survey of these results is found in the book by Cesari [1]. For higher-order systems, the results are more complex. There is the "Principle of Torus" which is used in the investigation of periodic oscillation for the system of the form

$$\dot{x} = X(x)$$

where x is an n-vector. This principle essentially generalizes the idea of the Poincaré-Bendixson theorem for higher dimensions. It is based upon the existence of a toroidal region R bounded by a smooth (n-1)-dimensional surface in the phase space such that all trajectories enter the region R as t increases. However, this principle has not been successfully employed for showing the existence of limit cycles for the system (6). The reader is recommended to consult Pliss [1] on the Principle of Torus. Zubov [1] considers the limit cycles for system (5) via Liapunov-type functions and toroidal regions.

4. *Boundedness and Ultimate Boundedness*

The forced as well as unforced van der Pol equation

$$\ddot{x}_1 + \varepsilon\dot{x}_1(x_1^2 - 1) + x_1 = p(t) \tag{21}$$

has been extensively studied by several researchers. This system is very rich in periodic phenomena, in particular subharmonics.* It may be observed that equation (21) does not admit harmonic solutions. Cartwright and Littlewood [1] give "almost" exact information as to the existence of subharmonics for the case when $p(t) = A \sin \omega t$ in terms of a parameter $\nu = A/\varepsilon\omega$. They have shown that for

$$1/100 < \nu < 2/3 - 1/100 \quad ,$$

stable subharmonic solutions of odd integral order exist except for certain small subintervals in the range (1/100, 2/3 - 1/100) which are transition regions. Levinson [2] has considered the equation

$$\ddot{x}_1 + \mu f_1(x_1)\dot{x}_1 + x_1 = A \sin t \quad ,$$

where $f(x_1) = 1$ for $x_1^2 > 1$ and $f(x_1) = -1$ for $x_1^2 \leq 1$, and has shown a behavior similar to the one shown by Cartwright and Littlewood for the van der Pol equation.

Information as precise as that of Cartwright and Littlewood or Levinson about the solution of nonlinear systems is indeed rare. Instead, attempts have been made to derive conditions for the existence of closed and bounded regions which exhibit the ultimate behavior of trajectories. The finding of such regions enables one to compute bounds on the amplitude of oscillation and the qualitative properties of the solution. There are several concepts asso-

---

* If the period of the forcing function $p(t)$ is τ, then a solution with period $n\tau$, n a positive integer, is a subharmonic of order n. Harmonics are periodic solutions with period τ/n, n a positive integer greater than or equal to 2.

ciated with the boundedness of trajectories. In the following, definitions are presented, and various concepts are illustrated by several examples.

Consider the system

$$\dot{y} = Y(y,t) \quad , \tag{22}$$

where y is an n-vector and $Y(0,t) = 0$ for all t.

Definition: Finite escape time. If there is a t_o and a y_o, $y(t_o,y_o,t_o) = y_o$ and a finite time T, $T \geq t_o$, such that

$$\|y(t,y_o,t_o)\| \to \infty \quad \text{as} \quad t \to T \quad ,$$

then the solution is said to have finite escape time.

Definition: Lagrange stability. The state $y(t,y_o,t_o)$ of the system (22) is said to be *bounded* for the initial condition (y_o,t_o) if there exists a constant b such that

$$\|y(t,y_o,t_o)\| \leq b \quad \text{for all} \quad t \geq t_o \quad .$$

If the solution $y(t,y_o,t_o)$ of the system (22) is bounded for every (y_o,t_o), then the system is said to be Lagrange stable. If b is independent of t_o, then the system is said to be *uniformly* Lagrange stable.

The system (2), which describes simple harmonic motion, is uniformly Lagrange stable and does not have a finite escape time.

Definition: Ultimately bounded. The system (22) is said to be ultimately bounded if there exists a constant $b > 0$, such that corresponding to each initial condition y_o, at $t = t_o$, there exists a time $t_{ob} \geq t_o$ such that

$$\|y(t,y_o,t_o)\| < b \quad \text{for all} \quad t > t_{ob}.$$

Let $\mathcal{B}$ denote the ball of norm b in n-dimensional space, in which all trajectories are ultimately bounded. This ball $\mathcal{B}$ is called the *region of ultimate boundedness*. Ultimate boundedness of trajectories in $\mathcal{B}$ does not exclude the existence of an initial condition such that the trajectory corresponding to this initial condition leaves the region $\mathcal{B}$ and ultimately enters $\mathcal{B}$ and never leaves again. In order to exclude the possibility of a trajectory leaving, and entering again, one considers the closed and bounded region Γ called the *region of ultimate confinement*. The region of ultimate confinement has the property that (i) for every initial condition y_o at $t = t_o$, there exists a $t_{o\Gamma} \geq t_o$ such that $y(t, y_o, t_o)$ is in Γ for all $t > t_{o\Gamma}$, and (ii) no trajectory leaves Γ; *i.e.*, $t_{o\Gamma} = t_o$ for every y_o in Γ. The behavior of trajectories with respect to the two regions described above is illustrated in Figures IV-6 and IV-7.

Certain authors do not distinguish between the regions of ultimate boundedness and confinement; however, the dis-

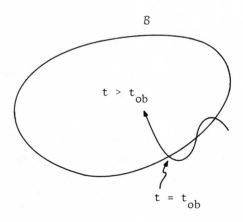

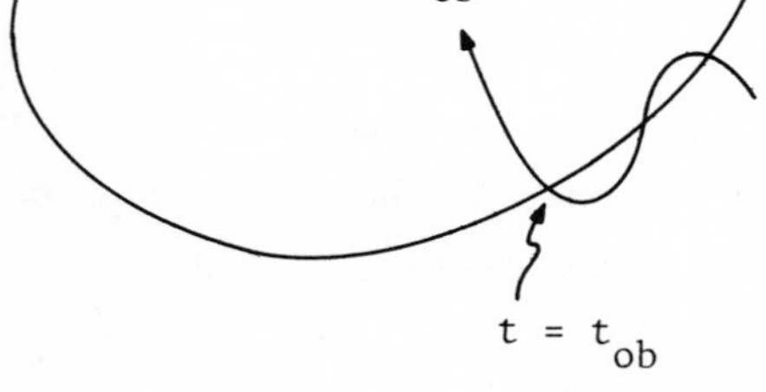

FIGURE IV-6: Region of ultimate boundedness.

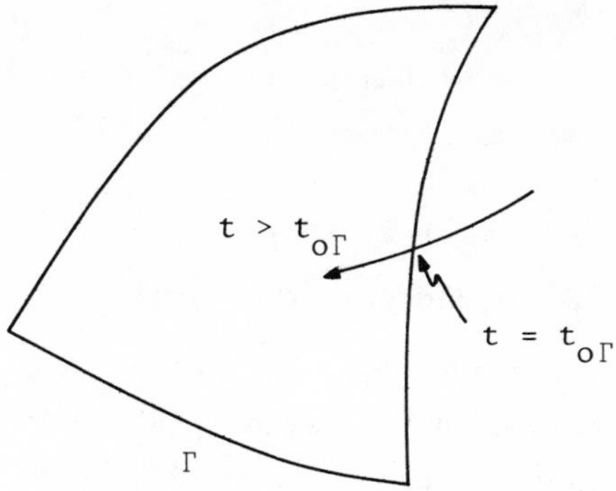

FIGURE IV-7: Region of ultimate confinement.

tinction is an important one. For example, for the van der Pol oscillator, a circle of sufficiently large radius is a region of ultimate boundedness but not a region of ultimate confinement.

For certain systems, it is possible to find a ball C in the n-dimensional state space such that all trajectories (excluding the trivial solution) are bounded away from this region. More precisely, there exists a constant c such that corresponding to every initial condition y_o at $t = t_o$ (excluding the trivial solution), there exists a $t_{oc} \geq t_o$ such that

$$\|y(t,y_o,t_o)\| > c \quad \text{for all} \quad t > t_{oc} .$$

The ball C of norm c is called the *region of ultimate "departure."* Similarly, one may define a region Σ in the state space such that for every y_o, (i) there exists a finite time $t_{o\Sigma}$ such that for $t > t_{o\Sigma}$, the trajectory

$y(t,y_o,t_o)$ lies outside the region Σ, and (ii) no trajectory enters Σ; *i.e.*, $t_{o\Sigma} = t_o$ for every y_o outside Σ. Σ is called the *region of ultimate "exclusion."*

Consider now the system

$$\dot{y} = Y(y,u,t) \tag{23}$$

where u is the input and y is the output.

Definition: Bibo stability. The system (23) is said to be bounded-input-bounded-output stable (Bibo stable) if for every bounded input, there is bounded output.*

It may be observed that asymptotic stability in the large of the system (23) with zero input does not imply Bibo stability. Obviously, asymptotic stability in the large implies Lagrange stability. This is illustrated in the following examples.

Example: Consider the system

$$\dot{x} = u(t) - f(x) \quad ,$$

where

$$f(x) = x \quad , \quad |x| \leq 1$$

$$f(x) = 1 \quad , \quad |x| > 1 \quad .$$

If $u(t) \equiv 0$, the system is asymptotically stable in the large. However, the system is unstable for $u(t) = 1 + \varepsilon$ where ε is some positive number.

Example: Consider the system

---

* It must be emphasized that y is considered as the output of the system. In this manner, the complication of the concept of observability of the unstable states of the system is avoided.

$$\dot{x} = -(1/(t+1))x(t) + u(t), \quad t > 0 .$$

The system is asymptotically stable in the large for $u(t) \equiv 0$; however, with $u(t) \equiv 1$, $|x(t)| \to \infty$ as $t \to \infty$.

In the case of second-order systems, the above properties of systems may be studied via geometric methods; however, in general, Liapunov-like methods are used in discussing them. The geometric and Liapunov-like methods are presented in the next two sections.

5. *Amplitude Bounds for Second-Order Systems*

For second-order systems, the trajectories are moving in the three-dimensional (y_1,y_2,t)-space. Under certain conditions, trajectories may eventually be confined in an infinitely long cylinder. The region Γ has the property of confining the trajectory of the point

$$(y_1(t,y_{1o},y_{2o},t_o),\ y_2(t,y_{1o},y_{2o},t_o)) \quad ,$$

which is the projection of the point

$$(y_1(t,y_{1o},y_{2o},t_o),\ y_2(t,y_{1o},y_{2o},t_o),\ t)$$

on the phase plane. A similar interpretation for the region Σ is possible.

Determination of regions Γ and Σ enables one to concentrate on a subset of the phase plane. Also, periodic trajectories, if they exist, lie inside Γ and outside Σ. This fact gives one a method for finding amplitude bounds on periodic solutions. In the case of a periodic forcing function, one may deduce from the existence of Γ the existence of one periodic solution with the same period as the forcing function, by using Brouwer's Fixed Point Theorem (see Cesari [1]).

Several researchers have considered the problem of finding the regions Γ and Σ. Ponzo and Wax [1] have used geometric methods in the study of the generalized van der Pol equation of the form

$$\begin{aligned} \dot{x}_1 &= x_2 - F(x_1) + p^*(t) \\ \dot{x}_2 &= -G(x_1) \quad , \end{aligned} \tag{24}$$

where $x_1G(x_1) > 0$, $x_1 \neq 0$, $x_1F(x_1) > 0$, $|x_1| >$ some $\tilde{x}_1$. The forced van der Pol equation (21) may be reduced to the above form (24) by the following substitution:

$$x_2 = \dot{x}_1 + F(x_1) - p(t),$$

where

$$F(x_1) = \int_0^{x_1} \varepsilon(u^2 - 1)\,du$$

and

$$p^*(t) = \int_0^t p(u)\,du \quad .$$

Ponzo and Wax have shown the existence of regions Γ and Σ for the general van der Pol equation under certain conditions.

The use of geometrical methods in the determination of amplitude bounds will be illustrated by finding the region Γ for the differential system

$$\begin{aligned} \dot{x}_1 &= x_2 - F(x_1) + p(t) \\ \dot{x}_2 &= -\mu x_1 \quad , \end{aligned} \tag{25}$$

where

(i) $\mu > 0$,

(ii) $p(\cdot)$ is continuous, and $|p(t)| \leq P$ for all t,

(iii) $F(x_1) = x_1^3/3 - x_1$.

The construction of a region of ultimate confinement is accomplished in two steps. The first part of the procedure consists in simplifying the given system so that the directions of trajectories for the given system are bounded by the directions of trajectories for the simplified system. Secondly, from the simplified system, contours are found which confine the trajectories of the original system. The details of the method are as follows.

The direction of trajectories of the system (25) at each point is bounded by the direction of the trajectories of the system

$$\left.\begin{array}{ll} \dot{x}_1 = x_2 - F(x_1) + P & \\ & \text{for } x_1 > 0 \;, \\ \dot{x}_2 = -\mu x_1 & \\ \dot{x}_1 = x_2 - F(x_1) - P & \\ & \text{for } x_1 < 0 \;, \\ \dot{x}_2 = -\mu x_1 & \end{array}\right. \tag{26}$$

and for $x_1 = 0$, the direction of trajectories is horizontal. Let

$$-f_+ = \min F(x_1) \quad , \quad x_1 \geq 0$$

$$f_- = \max F(x_1) \quad , \quad x_1 \leq 0 \quad .$$

The directions of the trajectories of the system (26) are bounded by the trajectories of the system

$$\left.\begin{array}{ll} \dot{x}_1 = x_2 + P_1 & \\ & \text{for } x_1 > 0 \;, \\ \dot{x}_2 = -\mu x_1 & \\ \dot{x}_1 = x_2 - P_2 & \\ & \text{for } x_1 < 0 \;, \\ \dot{x}_2 = -\mu x_1 & \end{array}\right. \tag{27}$$

where $P_1 = P + f_+$ and $P_2 = P + f_-$. The system (27) constitutes the simplified system. Consider the contours

$$x_2^2/2 + P_1 x_2 + \mu x_1^2/2 = \text{constant} = V \quad , \tag{28}$$

and the curve

$$-F(x_1) + x_2 + P = 0 \quad . \tag{29}$$

The contour (28) is obtained by integrating

$$\frac{dx_1}{dx_2} = \frac{x_2 + P_1}{-\mu x_1} \quad ,$$

obtained from (27) for $x_1 > 0$. For sufficiently large η, the contours passing through $(0,\eta)$ and $(0,-\eta)$ are monotonic outside the region $|x_2| \leq$ some η_0. A set of such contours are shown in Figure IV-8. The curve (29) is shown in Figure IV-9, where ε_0 is some positive number. The ε_0-square contains maxima and minima of the curve (29), and the function $x_2 = F(x_1) - P$ is monotonic in x_1 outside the ε_0-square. The curve (29) intersects the contour through $(0,\eta)$ at (ε_1,η_1); and the contour through $(0,-\eta)$ intersects the line $x_1 = \varepsilon_1$ at (ε_1,η_2) as shown in Figure IV-10. The coordinates of the points p_1 and p_2, in Figure IV-10, are given by the equations

$$\eta_1 = F(\varepsilon_1) - P_1 \tag{30}$$

$$\eta_1^2/2 + P_1\eta_1 + \mu\varepsilon_1^2/2 = \eta^2/2 + P_1\,\eta \tag{31}$$

$$\eta_2^2/2 + P_1\eta_2 + \mu\varepsilon_1^2/2 = \eta^2/2 - P_1\,\eta \quad . \tag{32}$$

Since F is a polynomial of degree 3,

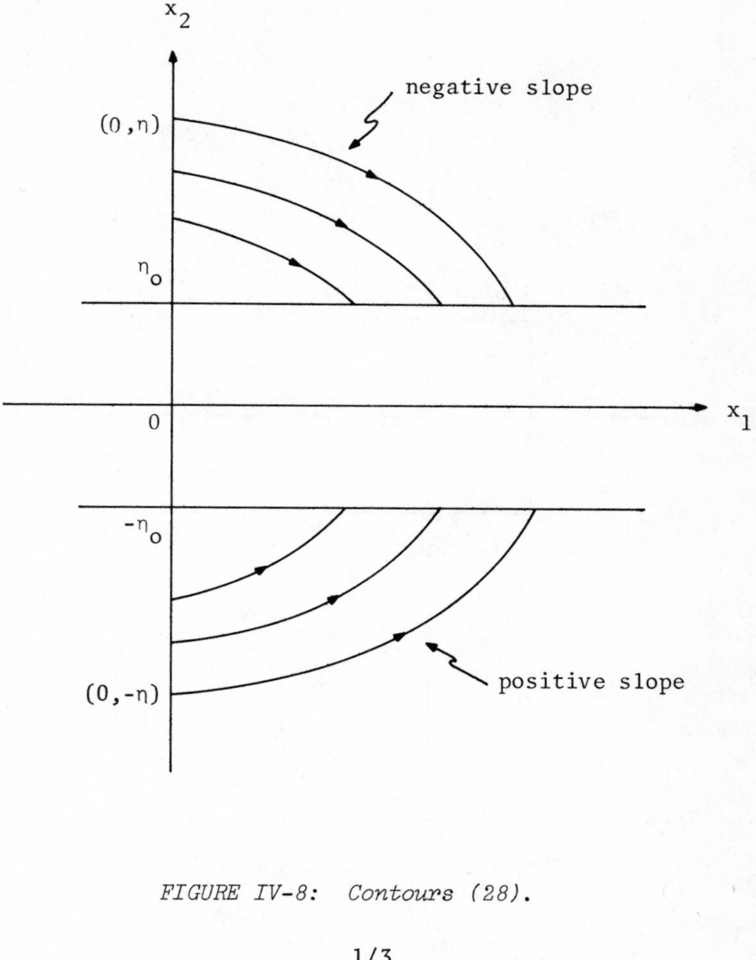

FIGURE IV-8: Contours (28).

$$\varepsilon_1 \approx \eta_1^{1/3}$$

$$\eta_1 \approx \eta$$

$$\eta_2 \approx -\eta \quad .$$

Thus, there exists η^* such that for all $\eta > \eta^*$,

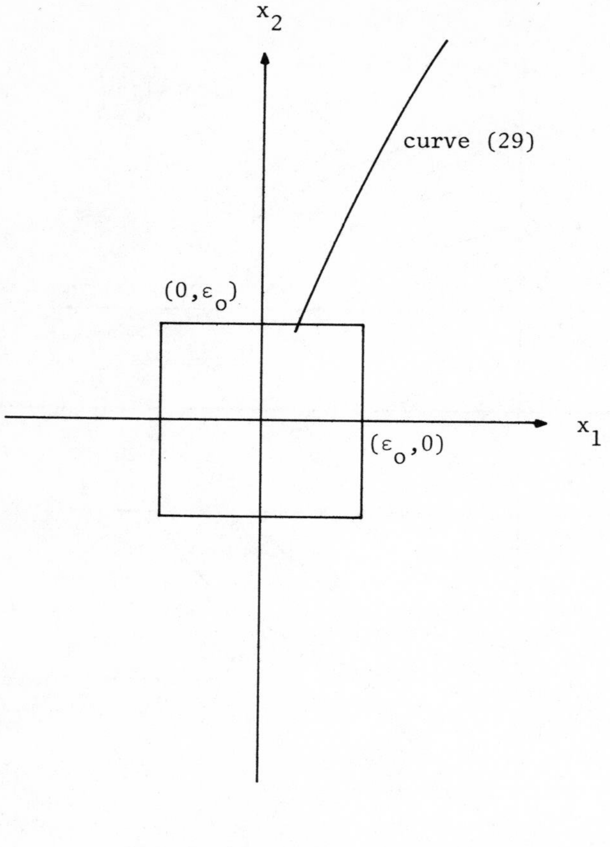

FIGURE IV-9: The curve (29).

$$-\eta_2 < \min\,(-\eta_o, -\varepsilon_o)$$

and

$$\eta_1 > \max\,(\varepsilon_o,\eta_o) \quad .$$

By simple geometrical arguments, it may be shown that the trajectories of the system (25) are crossing inward for all contours constructed as above with $\eta > \eta^*$. A similar contour may be constructed for $x_1 < 0$, and the trajectories

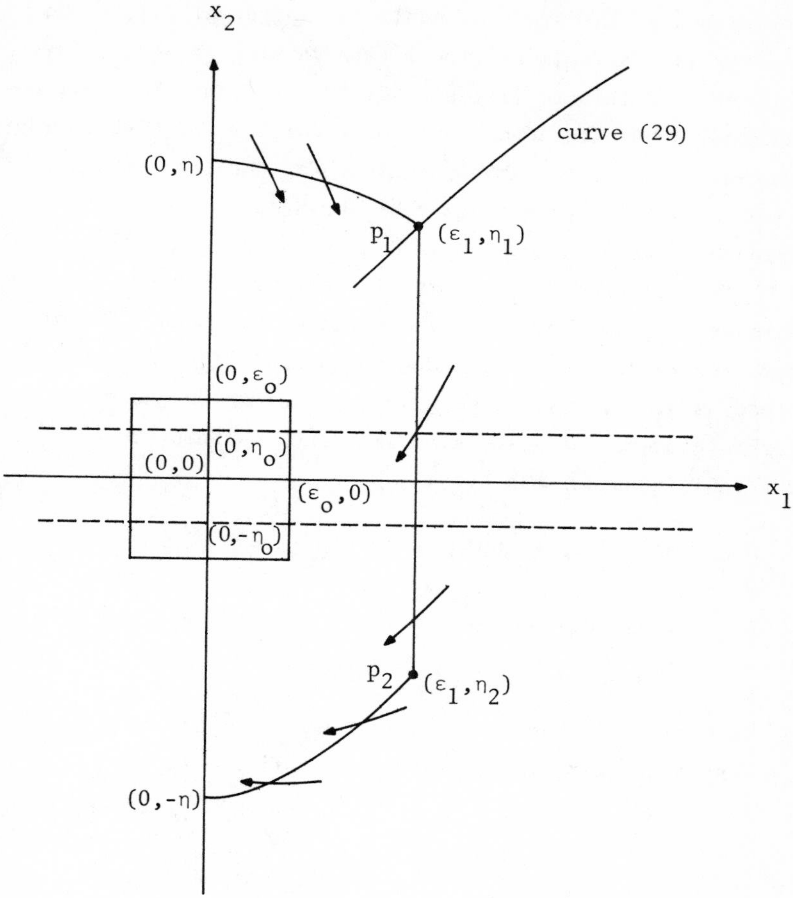

FIGURE IV-10: The bounding contour.

are moving horizontally at $x_1 = 0$; therefore, there exists a region Γ such that the trajectories are ultimately bounded in Γ.

Several authors have considered the application of such

techniques to the study of nonlinear (Aggarwal [3], Ponzo and Wax [1]) as well as linear time-varying (Brockett [2], Aggarwal and Infante [1]) second-order systems. However, geometrical arguments become extremely complex for higher-order systems. A more suitable technique for the investigation of coupled oscillators and other higher-order systems is a Liapunov-like method which is discussed in the next section.

The differential systems of the type discussed in this section are very rich in periodic phenomena. The interested reader is recommended to Hayashi [1] where the steady-state, transient behavior, subharmonics and other periodic phenomena associated with such systems are discussed in considerable detail.

Exercise 9: Show that the system

$$\dot{x} = -10.125\left(\frac{x^3}{3} - x\right) + y^3 + 10.125\, A_o \omega \sin \omega t$$

$$\dot{y} = -x$$

is ultimately bounded. Find a region of ultimate boundedness and a region of ultimate confinement.

$A_o = 0.3 \qquad \omega = 2.5$

$A_o = 0.25 \qquad \omega = 3.5$

$A_o = 0.35 \qquad \omega = 2.0$

Exercise 10: (Aggarwal [3]) For the system

$$\dot{x} = -x^3 + y + \sin 2t$$

$$\dot{y} = -x - y + 2 \sin 2.5t \quad ,$$

find regions similar to those of exercise 9.

Exercise 11: (Aggarwal [3]) For the system

$$\dot{x} = -x^3 + x + y^3 - y$$

$$\dot{y} = 0.125x^3 + 0.5x - y^3 + y \quad ,$$

find a region of ultimate confinement and a region of ultimate exclusion.

6. *Liapunov-Like Methods for Bounds*

The geometric method for finding the bounds of solutions for second-order systems was introduced in the last section, but the method described there is of limited applicability. The boundedness of systems in general may be studied via Liapunov-like methods. The purpose of this section is to develop these methods for the study of boundedness of solutions, as well as to apply these ideas to Bibo stability and ultimate confinement.

Lagrange stability theorem: Let Ω be a bounded region containing the origin and Ω^c denote the region outside Ω (*i.e.*, complement of the region Ω). If there exists a scalar function $V(y)$ with continuous partial derivatives, and continuous functions $a(r)$, $b(r)$ and $c(r)$ such that

(i) $a(\cdot)$, $b(\cdot)$ are non-decreasing and
$$0 < a(\|y\|) \le V(y) \le b(\|y\|) \text{ in } \Omega^c \quad ,$$

(ii) $c(\cdot)$ is non-decreasing and, along the solution,
$$\dot{V}(y) \le -c(\|y\|) \le 0 \text{ in } \Omega^c \quad ,$$

(iii) $a(r) \to \infty$ as $r \to \infty$,

then the system (22) is uniformly Lagrange stable.

Proof: The Lagrange stability theorem is similar to the asymptotic stability-in-the-large theorem of Section III.4 and the proof follows the same general reasoning. ◆

As before, the assumptions of the above theorem may be relaxed. For the system

$$\dot{y} = Y(y) \quad ,$$

the conditions reduce to $V(y) \to \infty$ as $\|y\| \to \infty$, and V has continuous partial derivatives such that $\dot{V} \leq 0$ for y in Ω^c.

Lur'e problem - restricted Bibo stability: Consider the Lur'e system with input shown in Figure IV-11. The system is described by the equations

$$\begin{aligned} \dot{x} &= Ax - b\phi(\sigma) \\ \sigma &= c'x + u \quad , \end{aligned} \tag{33}$$

where $\phi(\cdot)$ lies in the sector $(0,k]$; and the eigenvalues of A lie in the open left-hand plane. Suppose that there exists a Liapunov function of the form

$$V(x) = x'Px + \beta \int_0^\sigma \phi(u)\,du \tag{34}$$

for the unforced system (*i.e.*, $u(t) \equiv 0$) such that $\tilde{Q}$ is positive definite. $\tilde{Q}$ is defined in Section III.5. Varaiya

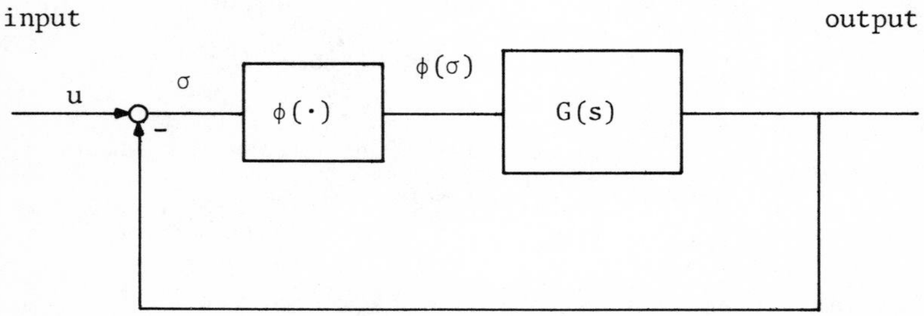

FIGURE IV-11: Lur'e system.

and Liu [1] have shown that such a system is bounded-output stable for every differentiable input such that u and $\dot{u}$ are bounded. This is a restricted type of Bibo stability. The result above follows by considering the derivative of the Liapunov function (34) along the solution of the system (33) and applying the theorem on Lagrange stability. The proof is left as an exercise for the reader.

Ultimate confinement theorem: Let Ω be a bounded region containing the origin and Ω^c denote the region outside Ω. If there exist a scalar function V(y) with continuous partial derivatives, and continuous functions a(r), b(r), c(r) such that

(i) $a(\cdot)$, $b(\cdot)$ are non-decreasing and
$0 < a(\|y\|) \leq V(y) \leq b(\|y\|)$ in Ω^c,

(ii) $c(\cdot)$ is non-decreasing and along the solution
$\dot{V}(y) \leq -c(\|y\|) < 0$ in Ω^c,

(iii) $a(r) \to \infty$ as $r \to \infty$,

then the system (22) has a region of ultimate confinement.

Proof: The proof follows the general reasoning as given in Section III.4. Here again the assumptions on V, a, b, and c in the above theorem may be relaxed. ◆

The application of this theorem to systems of higher order is no trivial matter because of the inability to find suitable V(y). This difficulty is illustrated by the following example.

Example: Consider the coupled Liénard equations:

$$\ddot{x}_i + f_i(x_i) + g_i(x_1, x_2, \ldots, x_n) = 0 \quad , \qquad (35)$$

$i = 1, \ldots, n$, where $g_i(x_1, x_2, \ldots, x_n) = \partial U/\partial x_i$, and

$\cup(x_1,\ldots,x_n)$ is a positive definite function of x. Liénard's equation (35) may be written as

$$\dot{x} = y - F(x)$$

$$\dot{y} = -G(x) \tag{36}$$

$$F_i(x_i) = \int_0^{x_i} f_i(u)\,du \;, \quad i = 1,\ldots,n,$$

where x, y are n-vectors and

$$F(x) = \begin{bmatrix} F_1 \\ \vdots \\ F_n \end{bmatrix} \qquad G(x) = \begin{bmatrix} g_1 \\ \vdots \\ g_n \end{bmatrix} .$$

LaSalle and Lefschetz [1] have investigated the boundedness of a single Liénard equation by using a function

$$(1/2)(y_1 - h_1(x_1))^2 + \int_0^{x_1} g_1(u)\,du \;, \tag{37}$$

where

$$h_1(x_1) = \begin{cases} c \;, & x > \alpha \\ (c/\alpha)x \;, & |x| \leq \alpha \\ -c \;, & x < -\alpha \end{cases} ,$$

c and α are constants.

A natural generalization of this function is

$$(1/2)\,[y - H(x)]'\,[y - H(x)] + \cup(x) \tag{38}$$

where

$$H(x) = \begin{bmatrix} h_1 \\ \vdots \\ h_n \end{bmatrix} ,$$

$$h_i(x_i) = \begin{cases} c \ , & x_i > \alpha \\ (c/\alpha)x_i \ , & |x_i| \leq \alpha \\ -c \ , & x_i < -\alpha \end{cases} \quad , \ i = 1,\ldots,n \ .$$

This function has been employed by deFigueiredo and Chang [1], and they give a sufficient set of conditions for ultimate confinement. In general, Liapunov-like functions yield conservative results. It is not obvious how a more suitable choice of V satisfying the conditions in the theorem on ultimate confinement may be made. This is a fundamental problem in the application of all Liapunov-like methods.

The regions of ultimate exclusion for coupled van der Pol oscillators have been considered by Aggarwal and Richie [1] and for a single oscillator by Ponzo and Wax [1].

Finally, examples are considered below which illustrate the difference between the usage of the theorems on Lagrange stability and ultimate boundedness.

Example: Consider the system

$$\dot{x} = -e^{-t} x \quad , \qquad x(0) = x_o \ .$$

The solution is given as

$$x(t) = x_o \exp(e^{-t} - 1) \ ,$$

and as $t \to \infty$, $x(t) \to x_o/e$. Let us examine the properties of the system via the positive definite function

$$V(x) = x^2 \ .$$

The derivative of V(x) along the solution is

$$\dot{V}(x) = -2 x^2 e^{-t} \ .$$

Now $\dot{V} < 0$, and $\dot{V} \to 0$ as $t \to \infty$. In this case, a function

$c(r)$ does not exist such that $\dot{V} \leq -c(\|y\|) < 0$. The system is stable but not asymptotically stable. Further, the system is Lagrange stable, but does not have a region of ultimate boundedness or confinement.

Example: The system

$$\dot{x} = -x^3 + x$$

may be studied via the positive definite function

$$V(x) = x^2 \quad .$$

The derivative of $V(x)$ along the solution is $2x^2(1-x^2)$. A simple application of the theorem on ultimate confinement yields that the solution is ultimately confined and

$$|x| < 1 + \varepsilon \ ,$$

where ε is a positive number.

Exercise 12: For the Rayleigh's oscillator

$$\ddot{x} + A_1 \dot{x}^3 - B_1 \dot{x} + x = 0 \quad , \quad A_1, B_1 > 0 \ ,$$

find a region of ultimate exclusion by considering the positive definite function $(\dot{x}^2 + x^2)/2$.

Exercise 13: (Aggarwal and Richie [1]) Coupled Rayleigh's oscillators are described by

$$\ddot{x} + A_1 \dot{x}^3 - B_1 \dot{x} + \alpha(x-y) = 0$$

$$\ddot{y} + A_2 \dot{y}^3 - B_2 \dot{y} + \alpha(x-y) = 0 \quad ,$$

A_1, A_2, B_1, B_2, and $\alpha > 0$. For these coupled oscillators, find a region of ultimate exclusion by considering the positive definite function $\dot{x}^2/2 + \dot{y}^2/2 + \alpha(x-y)^2/2$.

Exercise 14: Does the system

$$\dot{x}_1 = x_2 - \left(\frac{1.667}{5} x_1^5 - \frac{3.01}{3} x_1^3 + .01x_1 \right)$$

$$\dot{x}_2 = -x_1 - 10(x_1 - x_3)$$

$$\dot{x}_3 = x_4 - 5\left(\frac{x_3^3}{3} - x_3 \right)$$

$$\dot{x}_4 = -x_3 + 10(x_1 - x_3)$$

have a region of ultimate exclusion?

Exercise 15: Does the system

$$\dot{x}_1 = x_2 - (x_1^3/3 - x_1)$$

$$\dot{x}_2 = -x_1 - 10(x_1 - x_3)$$

$$\dot{x}_3 = x_4 - 5(x_3^3/3 - x_3)$$

$$\dot{x}_4 = -x_3 + 10(x_1 - x_3)$$

have a region of ultimate exclusion?

CHAPTER V

APPROXIMATION METHODS

1. *Introduction*

The qualitative behavior of nonlinear systems has been the subject of study in the last two chapters. Now we shall consider various qualitative as well as quantitative methods which depend upon the presence of a small parameter in the differential equations describing the system. In contrast to the qualitative methods, the quantitative methods are concerned with the determination of the solution to the system as an approximate explicit expression. The presence of the small parameter enables one to determine the behavior of the nonlinear system in terms of simpler systems. The literature on these approximation methods, for the solution of nonlinear problems, is vast, both in amount and diversity. Two broad classes of approximation methods are discussed in this chapter:

(i) small-parameter methods;

(ii) singular perturbation methods.

Small-parameter methods have been investigated since Poincaré [2], and, more recently, significant contributions have been made by Hale [1] and Cesari [1]. These methods are applied to systems of the form

$$\dot{x} = X(x,t,\varepsilon) \quad , \tag{1}$$

where x is an n-vector, ε is a small parameter, and the right-hand side of (1) is continuously differentiable in all its arguments. In general, the objective of small-parameter methods is to determine the behavior of the system (1) from the behavior of the system

$$\dot{x} = X(x,t,0) \quad , \tag{2}$$

i.e., the system corresponding to $\varepsilon = 0$.

An important subclass of these systems is that of quasilinear systems of the form

$$\ddot{x}_i + \omega_i^2 x_i = \varepsilon f_i(x_i,\dot{x}_i,t,\varepsilon),\ i = 1,2,\ldots,n, \tag{3}$$

or

$$\dot{x} = Ax + \varepsilon f(x,t,\varepsilon) \quad , \tag{4}$$

where ε is a small parameter, A is a constant matrix, $\omega_i > 0$, $i = 1,\ldots,n$, and x is an n-vector. The term *quasilinear* arises from two observations: (i) the system is linear when $\varepsilon = 0$; (ii) the behavior of the nonlinear system for sufficiently small ε is similar to the behavior of the linear system corresponding to $\varepsilon = 0$. Small-parameter methods, as applied to quasilinear systems, are aimed at determining periodic solutions for autonomous (time-invariant) systems or for periodically forced nonautonomous (time-varying) systems, and developing explicit closed forms of approximate solutions. These methods are discussed in the first part of this chapter.

Singular perturbation methods are applicable to systems of the form

$$\begin{aligned} \dot{x} &= f(t,x,y,\varepsilon) \\ \varepsilon\dot{y} &= g(t,x,y,\varepsilon) \quad , \end{aligned} \tag{5}$$

where x and y are vectors, ε is a small parameter and f and g are continuously differentiable in all their arguments. Here, interest lies in the determination of the behavior of the system (5) from the behavior of the system

$$\begin{aligned} \dot{x} &= f(t,x,y,0) \\ 0 &= g(t,x,y,0) \quad , \end{aligned} \tag{6}$$

i.e., the system corresponding to $\varepsilon = 0$. Earlier work on these systems was centered around the study of van der Pol's equation,

$$\ddot{y} + \mu\dot{y}(y^2 - 1) + y = 0 \quad , \tag{7}$$

containing the large parameter μ, which may be reduced to the form (5). For the case when $\mu >> 1$, the system (7) exhibits oscillatory behavior called relaxation oscillations. Earlier methods on relaxation oscillations are discussed by Andronow and Chaikin [1], Cartwright [1], and Dorodnicyn [1]. More recently, significant contributions in the theory of singular perturbation methods have been made by Tihonov [1], Miščenko [1] and Pontryagin [1]. The singular perturbation method is discussed in the latter part of this chapter.

The vast and varied literature on approximation techniques for quasilinear systems and singular perturbation makes a complete discussion of the methods unfeasible for the present *Notes*. However, a bibliography of major sources is presented in the last section of this chapter.

2. *Existence of Periodic Solutions*

Let $\hat{x}(t)$ denote a periodic solution of (2). As it was presented in Chapter III, the stability of the trajectory $\hat{x}(t)$ may be discussed by defining a new variable $y(t)$,

$$x(t) = y(t) + \hat{x}(t) \quad , \tag{8}$$

and considering the stability of the trivial solution of

$$\dot{y} = Y(y,t) \quad . \tag{9}$$

$Y(y,t)$ is determined by expanding $X(y(t) + \hat{x}(t),t,0)$ about $X(\hat{x}(t),t,0)$. If one neglects higher-order terms in y, (9) may be expressed as

$$\dot{y} = X_x(\hat{x}(t),t,0)y \quad , \tag{10}$$

where

$$X_x = \begin{bmatrix} \frac{\partial X_1}{\partial x_1} & \cdots & \frac{\partial X_1}{\partial x_n} \\ \frac{\partial X_2}{\partial x_1} & & \vdots \\ \vdots & & \\ \frac{\partial X_n}{\partial x_1} & \cdots & \frac{\partial X_n}{\partial x_n} \end{bmatrix} \quad .$$

The differential equation (10) is called the equation of first variation of (2).

The conditions for the existence of a periodic solution for the system (1) and the nature of these periodic solutions, given that ε is small and there is a periodic solution for (2), are numerous. The nature of these results depends broadly upon the following properties:

(i) Explicit dependence on t of the function $X(x,t,0)$;

(ii) Stability of the trivial solution of the system (10);

(iii) Existence of periodic solutions for the system (10).

Various results are obtained depending upon the nature of the assumptions concerning these three properties. In the following, one such result is presented.

Theorem: The quasilinear system

$$\dot{x} = Ax + \varepsilon f(x,t,\varepsilon) \quad , \tag{11}$$

where

(i) A is a constant $n\times n$ matrix with eigenvalues in the open left half plane,

(ii) $f(x,t,\varepsilon)$ is continuously differentiable in each of its arguments and periodic in t, *i.e.*,

$$f(x,t+T,\varepsilon) = f(x,t,\varepsilon) \quad ,$$

has a periodic solution with period T.

Proof: The solution $x(t,x_o,\varepsilon)$ to the system (11) with initial condition x_o at $t = 0$ is periodic with period T provided that

$$x(T,x_o,\varepsilon) = x(0,x_o,\varepsilon) = x_o$$

or

$$x(T,x_o,\varepsilon) - x_o = 0 \quad . \tag{12}$$

The equation (12) has the trivial solution $x_o = 0$ for the case of $\varepsilon = 0$. This corresponds to the trivial solution of

$$\dot{x} = Ax \quad ,$$

which is periodic with period T. The purpose of the theorem

is to show that (12) has a solution, denoted by $x_o(\varepsilon)$, for $|\varepsilon| \leq \varepsilon_o$, where ε_o is a sufficiently small positive number.

Let us assume that the Jacobian (with respect to x_o) of the left-hand side of (12) is nonsingular at $\varepsilon = 0$. Then a simple application of the Implicit Function Theorem (see Courant [1]) shows that there exists a unique continuously differentiable function $x_o(\varepsilon)$, defined for $|\varepsilon| < \varepsilon_o$ where ε_o is a sufficiently small positive number, such that $x_o = x_o(\varepsilon)$ is the solution to (12). Thus, the existence of a periodic solution for (11) depends upon the nonsingularity of the Jacobian

$$\left.\frac{\partial(x(T,x_o,\varepsilon) - x_o)}{\partial x_o}\right|_{\varepsilon = 0} .$$

In order to determine the conditions for the nonsingularity of the Jacobian, let us consider the matrix

$$\tilde{X}(t,x_o,\varepsilon) = \frac{\partial x(t,x_o,\varepsilon)}{\partial x_o} . \qquad (13)$$

The Jacobian is nonsingular provided that

$$\det(\tilde{X}(t,0,0) - I) \neq 0 . \qquad (14)$$

On differentiating (13) and evaluating the expression for $x_o = 0$ and $\varepsilon = 0$, one obtains

$$\frac{d}{dt}\tilde{X}(t,0,0) = A\tilde{X}(t,0,0) . \qquad (15)$$

The initial condition for $\tilde{X}(t,0,0)$ is obtained by observing that $x(0,x_o,\varepsilon) = x_o$, from which differentiation gives $\tilde{X}(0,0,0) = I$. The solution to (15) is given by

$$\tilde{X}(t,0,0) = e^{At} . \qquad (16)$$

Thus, the condition for nonsingularity of the Jacobian reduces to

$$\det(e^{AT} - I) \neq 0 \quad , \tag{17}$$

which is satisfied if the eigenvalues of A are in the open left-half plane. Therefore, the conditions (i) and (ii) above are sufficient for the existence of a periodic solution of period T, for sufficiently small ε.◆

Example: For the system

$$\ddot{x} + k\dot{x} + \omega^2 x = -\varepsilon x^3 - \varepsilon F \cos \lambda t \quad , \tag{18}$$

where $k > 0$, $\omega^2 > 0$, and $F \neq 0$ is a real constant, the conditions above are satisfied, and therefore there exists a periodic solution with period $2\pi/\lambda$. For $k < 0$, a similar observation may be made by reversing time and considering the modified system.

Exercise 1: Show that the following properties of the periodic solution hold for the system (11), subject to the conditions of the theorem above:

(i) The periodic solution is unique;

(ii) The periodic solution is nontrivial provided that the origin is not a singular point of the quasilinear system (11) for sufficiently small $|\varepsilon|$;

(iii) The periodic solution is asymptotically stable.

Exercise 2: Show that there exists a periodic solution for the system

$$\ddot{x} + k\dot{x} + \omega^2 x = -\varepsilon F \cos \lambda t, \qquad k > 0 \quad , \tag{19}$$

and verify this observation by finding this solution explicitly. Discuss the stability of this solution.

Exercise 3: Discuss the conditions for the existence of periodic solutions for the system

$$\dddot{x} + k(a_2\ddot{x} + a_1\dot{x} + a_0 x) = - \varepsilon F \cos \lambda t \; . \qquad (20)$$

Exercise 4: Are the results of the theorem above applicable to systems of the form

$$\ddot{x} + \omega^2 x = \varepsilon f(x,\dot{x},t,\varepsilon) \qquad (21)$$

or

$$\ddot{x} + \omega^2 x = \varepsilon f(x,\dot{x}) \quad ? \qquad (22)$$

Exercise 5: Is the theorem above applicable to systems of the form

$$\dot{x} = Ax + \varepsilon f(x,\varepsilon) \quad ? \qquad (23)$$

The theorem above illustrates the basic ingredients and flavor of the results possible. Additional results are possible depending upon the properties mentioned above.

3. *Quasilinear Systems - Approximation Methods*

There are several approximation methods, and three of these are discussed in this section. Emphasis is placed on the discussion of the technique rather than the proof of convergence of the approximating series or the mathematical justification of a given method. The reader interested in details of justification and related topics may consult the references given. In this section, attention is devoted to the second-order system

$$\ddot{x} + x = \varepsilon f(x,\dot{x}) \quad . \qquad (24)$$

Generalization of the methods to higher-order systems are possible but messy except in the case of the Equivalent Linearization Method.

Perturbation methods.

A natural form of series solution for the system (24) is a power series in ε. The procedure in finding such a solution consists of the following steps:

(i) Assume that the series solution is of the form

$$x(t) = x_0(t) + \varepsilon x_1(t) + \varepsilon^2 x_2(t) + \ldots \qquad (25)$$

where $x_0(t)$ is the solution to the system corresponding to $\varepsilon = 0$.

(ii) Substitute this $x(t)$ into (24) and determine differential equations for $x_0(t)$, $x_1(t)$, $x_2(t)$, ..., by equating coefficients of equal powers of ε.

(iii) Solve the differential equations for $x_i(t)$, $i = 0, \ldots$, to determine the solution to the desired power of ε.

Step (ii) of the procedure above yields

$$\begin{aligned} &\ddot{x}_0(t) + \varepsilon \ddot{x}_1(t) + \varepsilon^2 \ddot{x}_2(t) + \ldots \\ &\quad + x_0(t) + \varepsilon x_1(t) + \varepsilon^2 x_2(t) + \ldots \qquad (26) \\ &\quad = \varepsilon f(x_0 + \varepsilon x_1, \ldots, \dot{x}_0 + \varepsilon \dot{x}_1 + \varepsilon^2 x_2 + \ldots) . \end{aligned}$$

On expanding the right-hand side of (26), one obtains

$$\ddot{x}_0(t) + \varepsilon\ddot{x}_1(t) + \varepsilon^2\ddot{x}_2(t) + \dots$$

$$+ x_0(t) + \varepsilon x_1(t) + \varepsilon^2 x_2(t) + \dots$$

$$= \varepsilon f(x_0,\dot{x}_0) + \varepsilon(\varepsilon x_1(t)+\dots)\left.\frac{\partial f}{\partial x}\right|_{\substack{x=x_0\\ \dot{x}=\dot{x}_0}} + \varepsilon(\varepsilon\dot{x}_1(t)+\dots)\left.\frac{\partial f}{\partial \dot{x}}\right|_{\substack{x=x_0\\ \dot{x}=\dot{x}_0}}$$

$$+ \dots \quad . \tag{27}$$

Equating coefficients with equal powers of ε on both sides of (27) gives the following differential equations for $x_0(t), x_1(t), \dots$:

$$\ddot{x}_0 + x_0 = 0$$

$$\ddot{x}_1 + x_1 = f(x_0,\dot{x}_0)$$

$$\ddot{x}_2 + x_2 = x_1 \left.\frac{\partial f}{\partial x}\right|_{\substack{x = x_0\\ \dot{x} = \dot{x}_0}} + \dot{x}_1 \left.\frac{\partial f}{\partial \dot{x}}\right|_{\substack{x = x_0\\ \dot{x} = \dot{x}_0}} \tag{28}$$

$$\vdots$$

There are several variations of the above method, each with its own pitfalls. The methods and their pitfalls will be illustrated by considering an example.

Example: The Rayleigh [1] equation

$$\ddot{x} + x = \varepsilon\left(\dot{x} - \frac{\dot{x}^3}{3}\right) \quad , \tag{29}$$

where $\varepsilon > 0$, will be used to illustrate the procedure above. On substituting a solution of the form (25) into (29), expanding the right-hand side by a Taylor series, equating coefficients of equal powers of ε, one obtains:

$$\ddot{x}_0 + x_0 = 0$$
$$\ddot{x}_1 + x_1 = \dot{x}_0 - \dot{x}_0^3/3 \qquad (30)$$
$$\ddot{x}_2 + x_2 = \dot{x}_1 (1 - \dot{x}_0^2)$$
$$\vdots \qquad .$$

These are linear differential equations and may be solved successively to obtain $x_0, x_1, \ldots$. Let the initial condition for (29) be

$$x(0) = A \qquad \dot{x}(0) = 0 \quad ;$$

then, a set of initial conditions for $x_0, x_1, x_2, \ldots$ are

$$x_0(0) = A \qquad \dot{x}_0(0) = 0$$
$$x_i(0) = 0 \qquad \dot{x}_i(0) = 0 \ , \quad i=1,\ldots \ . \qquad (31)$$

On solving the equations (30), one obtains

$$x_0(t) = A \cos t$$
$$x_1(t) = \frac{A(\frac{1}{4}A^2 - 1)}{2}(\sin t - t \cos t) - \frac{A^3}{32}\sin t + \frac{A^3}{96}\sin 3t$$
$$\vdots \qquad . \qquad (32)$$

The expression for $x_1(t)$ contains a term of the form $t \cos t$, called the "secular term" which increases in amplitude as $t \to \infty$. The presence of secular terms should not be construed to mean that the solution diverges. However, the presence of secular terms indicates an unsuitable choice of the form of solution. This is made more obvious by the consideration of the linear system

$$\ddot{x} + x = - \varepsilon x \quad . \tag{33}$$

Here, the exact solution is

$$A \cos \sqrt{1 + \varepsilon}\, t \quad , \tag{34}$$

whereas the method above yields

$$A \cos t - 1/2\, \varepsilon At \sin t + \ldots . \tag{35}$$

On expanding the exact solution (34) about $\varepsilon = 0$, one obtains

$$A \cos \sqrt{1 + \varepsilon}\, t \simeq A \cos t - 1/2\, \varepsilon At \sin t + \ldots . \tag{36}$$

Expression (35) is thus the same as that obtained by expanding the solution in a series. It may be noted that the exact solution (34) is periodic; however, this fact is not evident from the series (36). The series solution contains secular terms which mask the periodic nature of the solution. The appearance of secular terms is the main disadvantage of the method above, which is also called Poisson's method. In general, the presence of secular terms prevents the determination of periodic solutions as well as the periodic behavior of the system.

A variation of the Poisson's method is due to Lindstedt (see Cesari [1]). The procedure consists in removing the secular terms as they arise, as follows:

(i) Transform the independent variable t so that the solution, as a function of the new variable τ, is periodic with period 2π; *i.e.*, $\Omega t = \tau$ and $x(\tau) = x(\tau+2\pi)$.

(ii) Assume the solution and transformation frequency to be of the form:

$$x = x_0(\tau) + \varepsilon x_1(\tau) + \ldots \tag{37}$$

$$\Omega = \Omega_0 + \varepsilon\Omega_1 + \ldots \quad . \tag{38}$$

(iii) Equate coefficients of equal powers of ε and obtain linear equations.

The application of this procedure to (24) yields (here a superscribed dot indicates derivative with respect to τ)

$$\begin{aligned}
&(\Omega_0 + \varepsilon\Omega_1 + \varepsilon^2\Omega_2 + \ldots)^2(\ddot{x}_0 + \varepsilon\ddot{x}_1 + \varepsilon^2\ddot{x}_2 + \ldots) \\
&\quad + (x_0 + \varepsilon x_1 + \varepsilon^2 x_2 + \ldots) \\
&\quad = \varepsilon f(x_0 + \varepsilon x_1 + \varepsilon^2 x_2 \ldots, (\Omega_0 + \varepsilon\Omega_1 + \varepsilon^2\Omega_2 + \ldots) \\
&\qquad (\dot{x}_0 + \varepsilon\dot{x}_1 + \varepsilon^2\dot{x}_2 + \ldots)) \quad .
\end{aligned} \tag{39}$$

The right-hand side of (39) may be expanded as

$$\varepsilon f(x_0, \Omega_0\dot{x}_0) + \varepsilon^2 x_1 \left.\frac{\partial f}{\partial x}\right|_{\substack{x=x_0 \\ \dot{x}=\Omega_0\dot{x}_0}} + \varepsilon^2(\Omega_1\dot{x}_0 + \Omega_0\dot{x}_1) \left.\frac{\partial f}{\partial \dot{x}}\right|_{\substack{x=x_0 \\ \dot{x}=\Omega_0\dot{x}_0}} + \ldots \quad .$$

The equating of coefficients of equal powers of ε yields

$$\begin{aligned}
&\Omega_0^2\ddot{x}_0 + x_0 = 0 \\
&\Omega_0^2\ddot{x}_1 + 2\Omega_1\Omega_0\ddot{x}_0 + x_1 = f(x_0, \Omega_0\dot{x}_0) \\
&\Omega_0^2\ddot{x}_2 + \Omega_1^2\ddot{x}_0 + 2\Omega_2\Omega_0\ddot{x}_0 + x_2 \\
&\quad = x_1 \left.\frac{\partial f}{\partial x}\right|_{\substack{x = x_0 \\ \dot{x} = \Omega_0\dot{x}_0}} + (\Omega_1\dot{x}_0 + \Omega_0\dot{x}_1) \left.\frac{\partial f}{\partial \dot{x}}\right|_{\substack{x = x_0 \\ \dot{x} = \Omega_0 x_0}} \\
&\quad \vdots
\end{aligned} \tag{40}$$

.

Example: The procedure will be illustrated by considering Rayleigh's equation. On following the steps of Lindstedt's method, one obtains (again, a superscribed dot indicates derivative with respect to τ):

$$\Omega_0^2\ddot{x}_0 + x_0 = 0$$

$$\Omega_0^2\ddot{x}_1 + x_1 = \Omega_0\dot{x}_0 - 1/3\ \Omega_0^3\ x_0^3 - 2\Omega_0\Omega_1\ddot{x}_0$$

$$\Omega_0^2\ddot{x}_2 + x_2 = -2\Omega_0\Omega_1\ddot{x}_1 - (2\Omega_0\Omega_2+\Omega_1^2)\ddot{x}_0 - \Omega_0^2\Omega_1\dot{x}_0^3 - \Omega_0^3\dot{x}_0^2\dot{x}_1$$

$$+ \Omega_1\dot{x}_0 + \Omega_0\dot{x}_1$$

$$\vdots \qquad . \tag{41}$$

On solving the differential equation for x_0 in (41) with $x_0(0) = A_0$, $\dot{x}_0(0) = 0$, one obtains

$$x_0(\tau) = A_0 \cos \tau/\Omega_0 \quad ,$$

and the periodicity condition

$$x_0(\tau) = x_0(\tau + 2\pi)$$

implies that $\Omega_0 = 1$. Then substitution for x_0, in equation (41), yields

$$\ddot{x}_1 + x_1 = 2\Omega_1 A_0 \cos \tau - A_0 \sin \tau + \frac{A_0^3}{4} \sin \tau - \frac{A_0^3}{12} \sin 3\tau$$

$$= 2\Omega_1 A_0 \cos \tau - A_0\left(\frac{A_0^2}{4} - 1\right) \sin \tau - \frac{A_0^3}{12} \sin 3\tau \ .$$

In order to exclude the presence of secular terms in the solution of x_1, one must have

$$\Omega_1 = 0 \quad \text{and} \quad A_0^2 = 4 \ .$$

This gives

$$\ddot{x}_1 + x_1 = -2/3 \sin 3\tau \ . \tag{42}$$

The solution to equation (42) is

$$x_1(\tau) = A_1 \cos \tau + B_1 \sin \tau + \frac{1}{12} \sin 3\tau \ .$$

The constant B_1 may be evaluated by assuming $\dot{x}_1(0) = 0$, and in this case $B_1 = -1/4$. A_1 is determined in the next step, where the coefficient of $\sin \tau$ or $\cos \tau$ in the differential equation for x_2 is set to zero in order to exclude secular terms. This process may be continued and terms in the series for Ω and x may be determined. The initial condition for the solution is

$$x(0) = A_0 + \varepsilon A_1 + \ldots$$

$$\dot{x}(0) = 0 \ .$$

The first-order approximation is

$$\Omega_0 = 1$$

$$A_0 = 2$$

$$x_0(\tau) = 2 \cos \tau \ .$$

Lindstedt's method has a major pitfall of its own. Poincaré has shown that the series obtained by Lindstedt's method, in general, does not converge.

There is another variation of the perturbation method due to Poincaré which is more suitable for systems with "slow motion" like the motion of planets, and is omitted from the discussion here.

Averaging methods.

Consider again the quasilinear differential system (22). The solution to the corresponding linear system ($\varepsilon = 0$) is given by

$$x(t) = a \cos(\omega t + \phi) \quad , \tag{43}$$

where the amplitude a and phase angle ϕ are constants depending on the initial conditions. The method of averaging is based on the assumption that for small ε the form of the solution (43) does not change, but a and ϕ are slowly varying parameters. The procedure consists of assuming

$$x(t) = a(t) \cos(\omega t + \phi(t)) \ , \tag{44}$$

$$\dot{x}(t) = -a(t)\, \omega \sin(\omega t + \phi(t)) \ , \tag{45}$$

and

$$\dot{a}(t) \cos(\omega t + \phi(t)) - a(t)\, \dot{\phi}(t) \sin(\omega t + \phi(t)) = 0. \tag{46}$$

On evaluating $\ddot{x}$ from (22) and (45) and equating, one obtains

$$- \omega\dot{a}(t) \sin(\omega t + \phi(t)) - \omega a(t)\, \dot{\phi}(t) \cos(\omega t + \phi(t))$$

$$= \varepsilon f(a(t) \cos(\omega t + \phi(t)), - a(t)\, \omega \sin(\omega t + \phi(t)). \tag{47}$$

Solving for $\dot{a}$ and $\dot{\phi}$ from (46) and (47) gives

$$\begin{aligned} \dot{a} &= - \frac{\varepsilon}{\omega} f(a \cos \psi, - a\omega \sin \psi) \sin \psi \\ \dot{\phi} &= - \frac{\varepsilon}{\omega a} f(a \cos \psi, - a\omega \sin \psi) \cos \psi, \end{aligned} \tag{48}$$

where $\psi \triangleq \omega t + \phi(t)$. Under suitable conditions, the functions on the right-hand side of (48) may be expanded in Fourier series as

$$f(a\cos\psi, -a\omega\sin\psi)\sin\psi = \frac{1}{2}\alpha_0 + \sum_n (\alpha_n \cos n\psi + \beta_n \sin n\psi)$$

$$f(a\cos\psi, -a\omega\sin\psi)\cos\psi = \frac{1}{2}\alpha'_0 + \sum_n (\alpha'_n \cos n\psi + \beta'_n \sin n\psi), \tag{49}$$

where

$$\alpha_n = \frac{1}{\pi}\int_0^{2\pi} f(a\cos\psi, -a\omega\sin\psi)\sin\psi\cos n\psi\, d\psi$$

$$\beta_n = \frac{1}{\pi}\int_0^{2\pi} f(a\cos\psi, -a\omega\sin\psi)\sin\psi\sin n\psi\, d\psi$$

$$\alpha'_n = \frac{1}{\pi}\int_0^{2\pi} f(a\cos\psi, -a\omega\sin\psi)\cos\psi\cos n\psi\, d\psi$$

$$\beta'_n = \frac{1}{\pi}\int_0^{2\pi} f(a\cos\psi, -a\omega\sin\psi)\cos\psi\sin n\psi\, d\psi\ .$$

The constant terms in the Fourier expansion may be used to obtain the first approximation. Thus, the expressions for $\dot{a}(t)$ and $\dot{\phi}(t)$ are:

$$\dot{a}(t) \simeq -\frac{\varepsilon}{2\pi\omega}\int_0^{2\pi} f(a\cos\psi, -a\omega\sin\psi)\sin\psi\, d\psi$$

$$\tag{50}$$

$$\dot{\phi}(t) \simeq -\frac{\varepsilon}{2\pi\omega a}\int_0^{2\pi} f(a\cos\psi, -a\omega\sin\psi)\cos\psi\, d\psi\ .$$

This method is called the Kryloff and Bogoliuboff method.

A method very similar to this is the van der Pol approximation method. Here the solution is assumed to be in the form

$$x(t) = a(t) \cos \omega t + b(t) \sin \omega t$$

$$\dot{x}(t) = -a(t)\omega \sin \omega t + b(t)\omega \cos \omega t \tag{51}$$

and

$$\dot{a}(t) \cos \omega t + \dot{b}(t) \sin \omega t = 0 \quad .$$

Proceeding in a fashion similar to the Kryloff and Bogoliuboff method, one obtains

$$\dot{a} = -\frac{\varepsilon}{\omega} f(a \cos \omega t + b \sin \omega t, -a\omega \sin \omega t + \omega b \cos \omega t) \sin \omega t$$

$$\dot{b} = \frac{\varepsilon}{\omega} f(a \cos \omega t + b \sin \omega t, -a\omega \sin \omega t + \omega b \cos \omega t) \cos \omega t \ . \tag{52}$$

At this stage, one expands the right-hand side in Fourier series and proceeds as before. The methods of Kryloff and Bogoliuboff and van der Pol are the same, to the first degree of approximation.

Example: The procedure above will be illustrated by again considering Rayleigh's equation. Here $\dot{a}$ and $\dot{\phi}$ are given as:

$$\frac{da}{dt} = -\frac{\varepsilon}{\omega}\left(-a\omega \sin \psi + \frac{1}{3} a^3 \omega^3 \sin^3 \psi\right) \sin \psi$$

$$\frac{d\phi}{dt} = -\frac{\varepsilon}{a\omega}\left(-a\omega \sin \psi + \frac{1}{3} a^3 \omega^3 \sin^3 \psi\right) \cos \psi, \tag{53}$$

where

$$\psi = \omega t + \phi \text{ and } \omega = 1 \quad .$$

On approximating the right-hand sides by constant terms in the Fourier series expansions, one obtains

$$\frac{da}{dt} \approx \frac{\varepsilon}{2}\ a\ (1 - \frac{a^2}{4}) \qquad\qquad (54)$$

$$\frac{d\phi}{dt} \approx 0 \quad .$$

Integration of the approximate equations (54) with initial conditions a_o and ϕ_o at $t = 0$ yields

$$a(t) = a_o\ e^{\varepsilon t/2} / [1 + \frac{1}{4} a_o^2 (e^{\varepsilon t} - 1)]^{1/2} \qquad\qquad (55)$$

$$\phi(t) = \phi_o \quad .$$

Therefore, to the first degree of approximation

$$x(t) = \frac{a_o\ e^{\varepsilon t/2}}{[1 + \frac{1}{4} a_o^2 (e^{\varepsilon t} - 1)]^{1/2}} \cos (t + \phi_o) \quad . \qquad (56)$$

The asymptotic behavior of the system is given by $x(t) \approx 2 \cos (t + \phi_o)$ as $t \to \infty$. This result was obtained earlier via Lindstedt's method.

The approximate expressions obtained by the methods of Poisson, Lindstedt, and Kryloff and Bogoliuboff were programmed on a computer to obtain curves for the solution. Figures V-1 and V-2 show various approximate solutions and the numerical solution of Rayleigh's equation obtained by Nordsieck's [1] method. The initial condition for this solution is

$$x(0) = 2,\ \dot{x}(0) = 0 \quad .$$

It may be observed that Lindstedt's and the Kryloff and Bogoliuboff approximations are identical. Figure V-3 shows Poisson's and Kryloff and Bogoliuboff's approximations and the numerical solution for the initial conditions

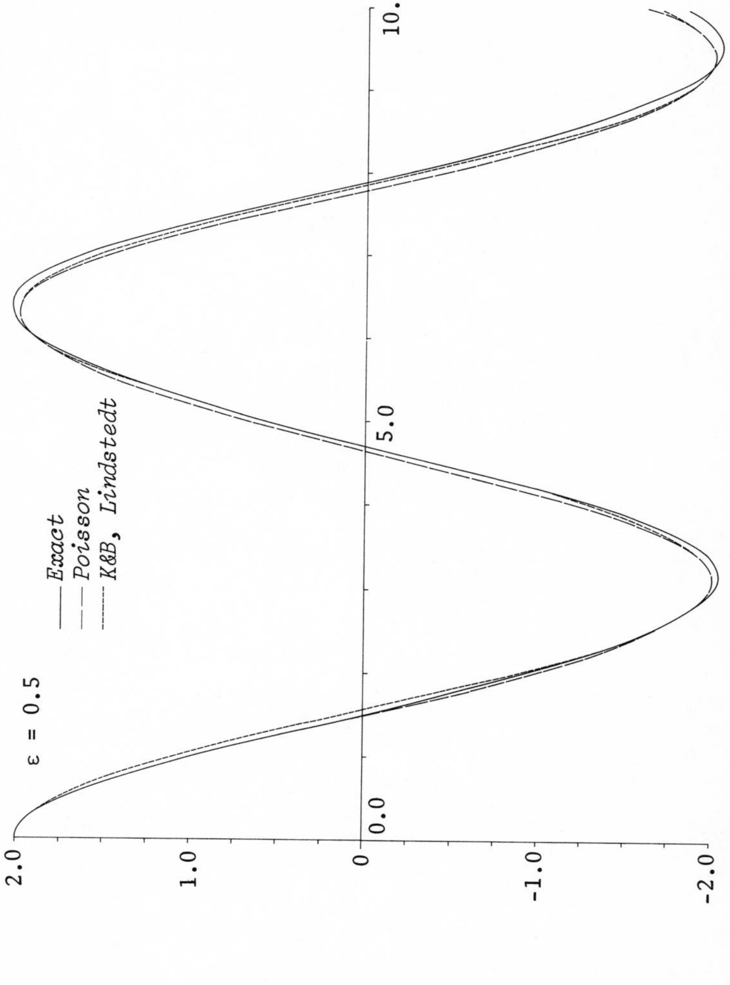

FIGURE V-1: Approximate solution for Rayleigh oscillator.

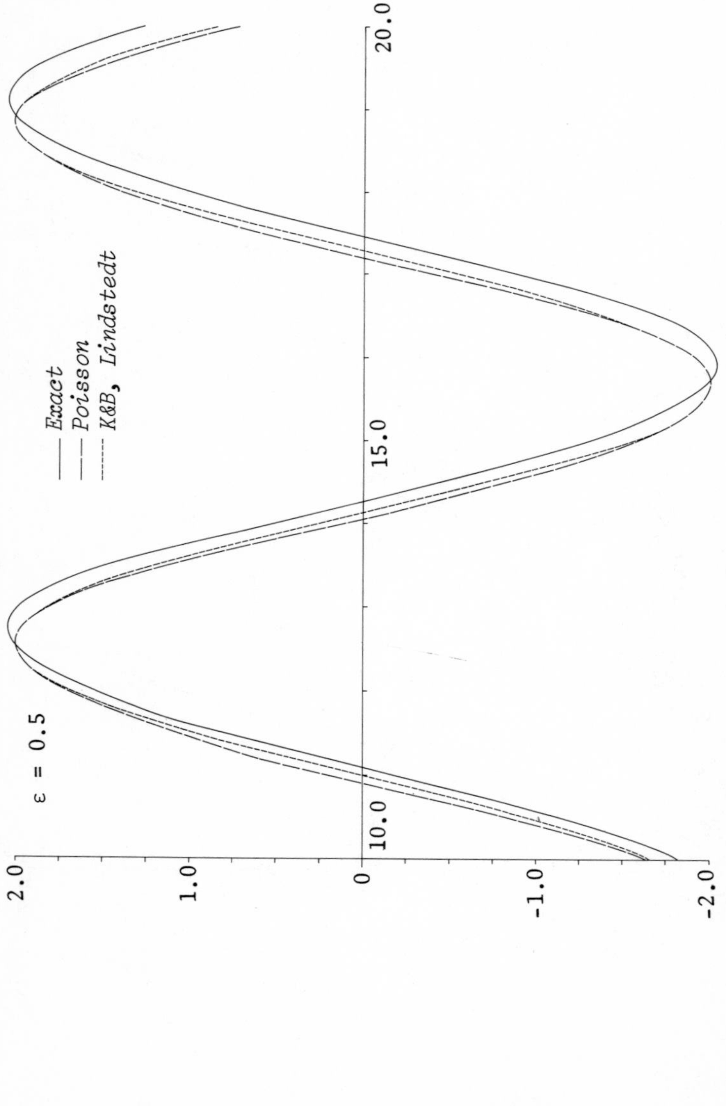

FIGURE V-2: Approximate solution for Rayleigh oscillator.

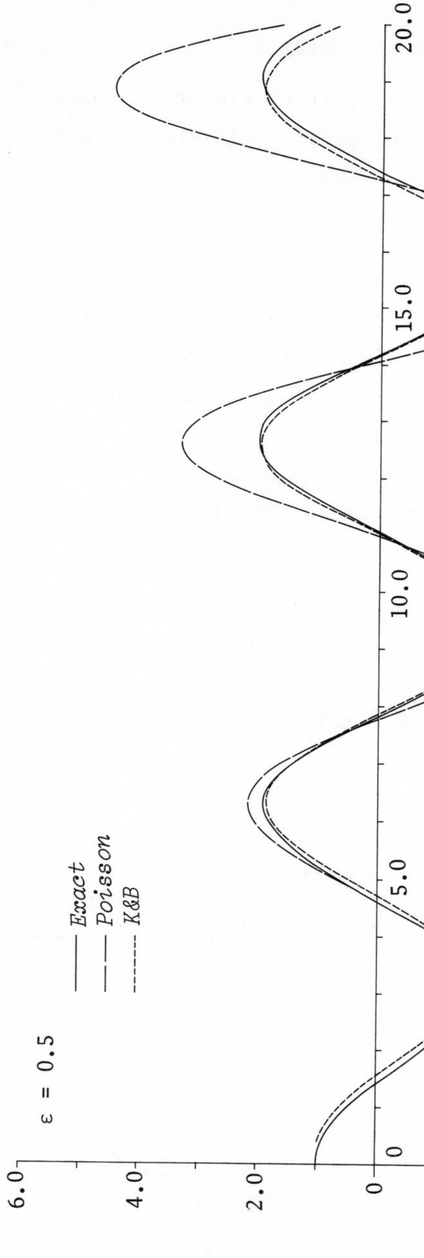

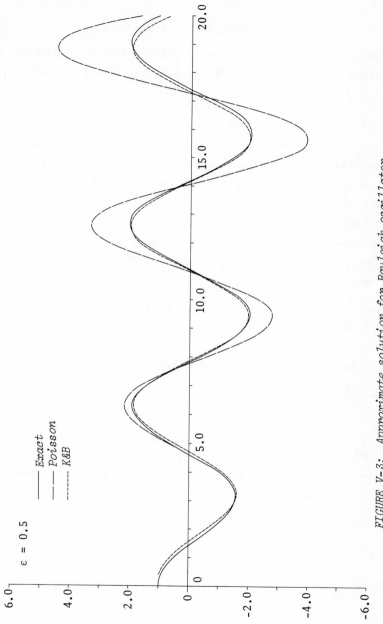

FIGURE V-3: Approximate solution for Rayleigh oscillator.

$$x(0) = 1, \quad \dot{x}(0) = 0 \quad .$$

The effect of secular terms is fairly evident in Poisson's method whereas the Kryloff and Bogoliuboff approximation is rather good.

Equivalent linearization method.

The perturbation and averaging methods discussed above are most suitable for second-order systems. Their application to higher-order systems is messy, to say the least. A method more suitable for computer investigation and graphical display of the characteristics of the system is the Equivalent Linearization method. An example is considered first to illustrate the procedure of the Equivalent Linearization method.

Example: Let us consider Rayleigh's differential system, however, now in the form of a closed-loop system as shown in Figure V-4, where $G(s) = \varepsilon/(s^2 - \varepsilon s + 1)$. It may be noted that G(s), the linear part of the system, is unstable.

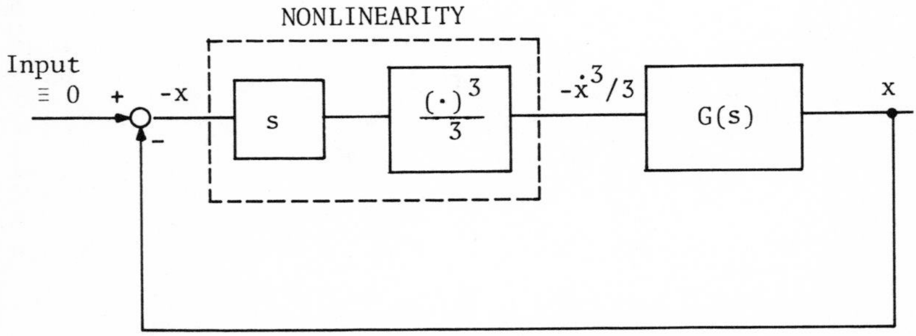

FIGURE V-4: Rayleigh's oscillator.

Let us consider the behavior of the nonlinearity to a sinusoidal input, as shown in Figure V-5a. The input is

$$a \sin \omega t \quad ,$$

and the output is

$$\frac{1}{3} a^3 \omega^3 \cos^3 \omega t = \frac{1}{3} a^3 \omega^3 \left(\frac{3}{4} \cos \omega t + \frac{1}{4} \cos 3\omega \right) \quad ,$$

which contains a third harmonic term cos $3\omega t$. Let us assume that the third harmonic is "suppressed" or "filtered out." This is indicated by introducing a filter as shown in Figure V-5b. The output of the nonlinearity together with the filter, called "the modified nonlinearity," is

$$\frac{1}{4} a^3 \omega^3 \cos \omega t \quad .$$

Thus the "describing function" (*i.e.*, the equivalent transfer function) of the modified nonlinearity is

$$N_{a,\omega}(s) = \frac{1}{4} a^2 \omega^2 s \quad .$$

Now consider the system shown in Figure V-6, where the modified nonlinearity has replaced the actual nonlinearity. The eigenvalues of the modified system in Figure V-6 are given by the roots of equation

$$1 + N_{a,\omega}(s)\, G(s) = 0 \quad . \tag{57}$$

The modified system will sustain oscillation at the frequency ω and amplitude a (at the input to the nonlinearity) if

$$1 + N_{a,\omega}(j\omega)\, G(j\omega) = 0 \quad . \tag{58}$$

In the present case, if $a = 2$ and $\omega = 1$, there is an oscillation for the modified system. Under suitable conditions, the oscillatory behavior of the modified system with the modified nonlinearity predicts the oscillatory behavior of the original system. In the case of the Rayleigh oscillator, the modified system has predicted the oscillatory behavior correctly. The procedure above may be generalized and is called the Equivalent Linearization method.

In general, consider system (24), with a nonlinearity which is symmetrical about the origin, and the modified system, as shown in Figure V-7 and V-8, respectively. By a nonlinearity which is symmetrical about the origin for system (24) it is meant that

$$-f(x,\dot{x}) = f(-x,-\dot{x}) \quad .$$

The characteristics of the nonlinearity and the filter may be defined by a scalar describing function $N_{a,\omega}(s)$. For the modified system to have an oscillation at frequency ω and amplitude a, one must have

$$N_{a,\omega}(j\omega)\ G(j\omega) = -1 \ . \tag{59}$$

A graphical solution of this equation is shown in Figure V-9 where, for a given a, the function $N_{a,\omega}(j\omega)\ G(j\omega)$ is plotted as a function of frequency. For oscillation, one is interested in the curve which passes through the point (-1,0).

The Equivalent Linearization method is an approximate technique and may fail under certain circumstances. An obvious way the method may fail is if the linear part G(s) does not suppress the harmonics sufficiently. In Chapter 3, we discussed Aizerman's conjecture and asserted that Aizerman's conjecture is not true. Several counter-exam-

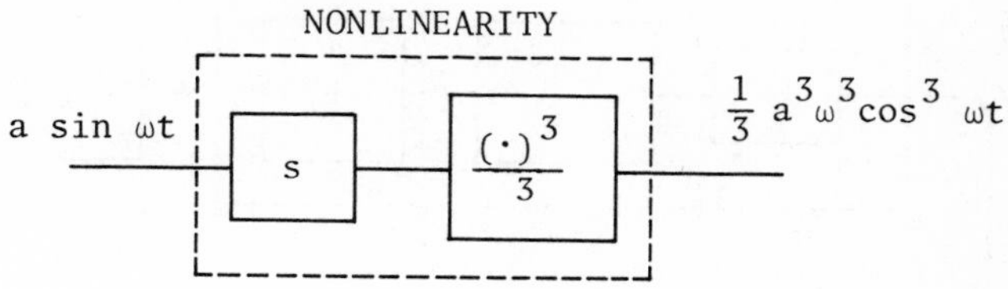

(a)

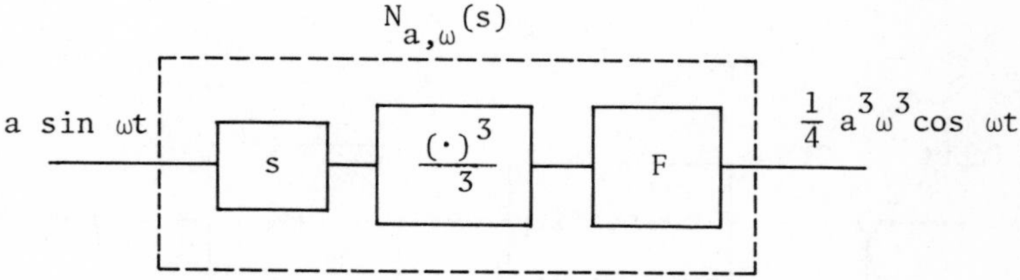

(b)

FIGURE V-5: (a) Nonlinearity.
(b) Modified nonlinearity.

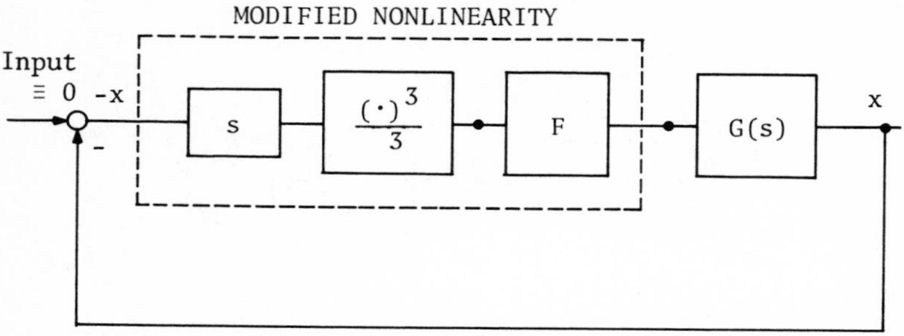

FIGURE V-6: Modified Rayleigh's oscillator.

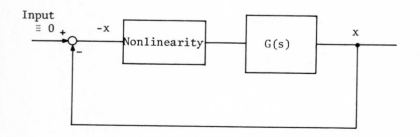

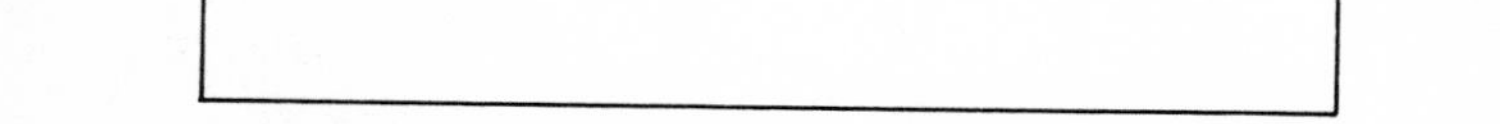

FIGURE V-7: Nonlinear system.

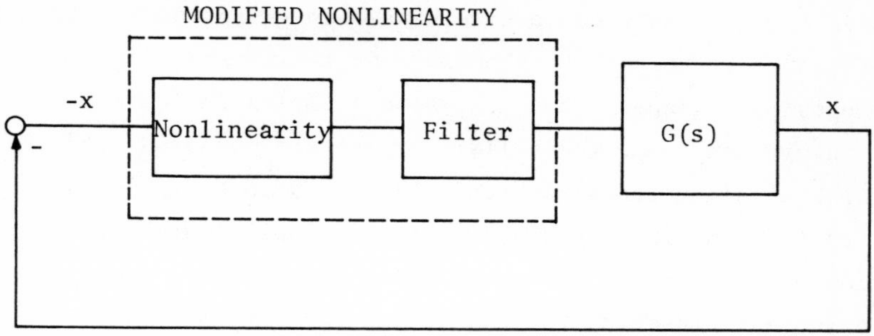

FIGURE V-8: Modified nonlinear system.

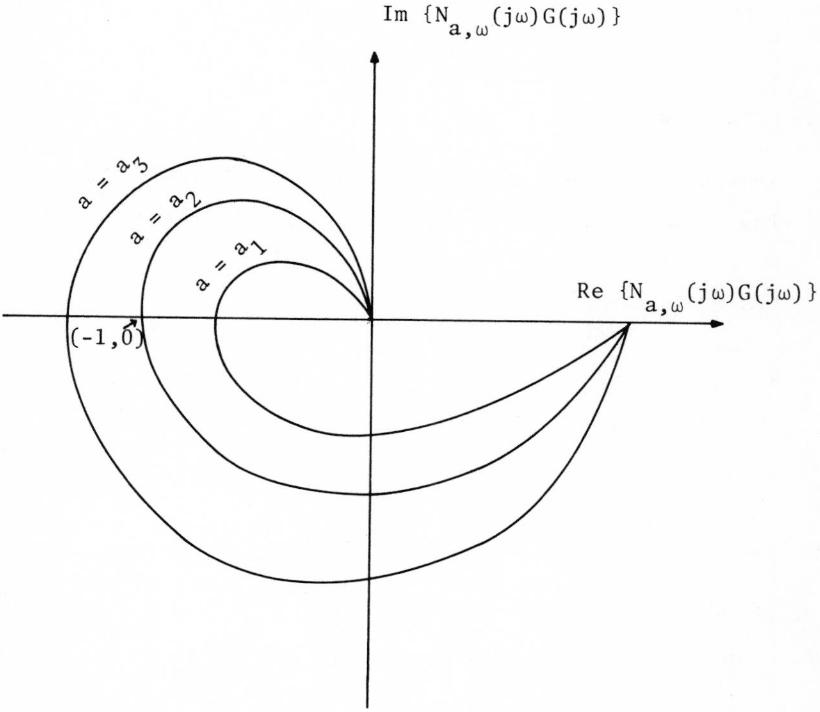

FIGURE V-9: Equivalent Linearization method.

ples to Aizerman's conjecture have been given, and failure of the conjecture happens because of the presence of limit cycles. It happens that for these examples (or rather counter-examples), these limit cycles are not predicted by the Equivalent Linearization method. These examples consitute an interesting class where the Equivalent Linearization method fails. The mathematical legitimacy of the Equivalent Linearization method for the system

$$\ddot{x} = f(x,\dot{x})$$

where x is a real n-vector and $f(x,\dot{x})$ is symmetrical about the origin,

$$-f(x,\dot{x}) = f(-x,-\dot{x}) \ ,$$

is discussed by Bass [1].

Exercise 8: Use the Poisson, Lindstedt, Kryloff and Bogoliuboff, van der Pol and Equivalent Linearization methods to study the approximate solution of the following systems:

(i) $\ddot{x} + k_1\dot{x} + k_2x + k_3x^3 = 0$

(ii) $\ddot{x} + k_1\dot{x}(x^2 - 1) + k_2x = 0$

(iii) $\ddot{x} + k_1\dot{x}(x^2 - 1) + k_2x + k_3x^3 = 0$.

Compare the result for various methods.

4. *Singular Perturbation Method*

The behavior of a van der Pol oscillator,

$$\ddot{y} + \mu(y^2 - 1)\dot{y} + y = 0 \ ,$$

for $\mu \gg 1$ is quite different from the behavior of the

quasilinear case, $\mu << 1$. The system exhibits "almost discontinuous" oscillations as $\mu \to \infty$, which are called *relaxation oscillations*. To illustrate this phenomenon, let

$$\mu x = \dot{y} + \mu(y^3/3 - y).$$

Then the van der Pol equation (7) reduces to

$$\dot{y} = \mu x - \mu(y^3/3 - y)$$

$$\mu \dot{x} = - y \quad .$$

On substituting $\varepsilon = 1/\mu$, one gets

$$\begin{aligned} \dot{x} &= -\varepsilon y \\ \varepsilon \dot{y} &= x - (y^3/3 - y) \quad , \end{aligned} \tag{60}$$

where $\varepsilon << 1$. Figure V-10 shows several trajectories obtained by the computer integration of the differential equations (60). The trajectories consist essentially of two types of curves: (i) vertical line segments, and (ii) portions of the curve $x = y^3/3 - y$. This is also seen by observing that in the (x,y)-plane

$$\frac{dx}{dy}\,(x - (y^3/3 - y)) = -\varepsilon^2 y \quad ,$$

and for sufficiently small ε, either $\frac{dx}{dy}$ is small or $x - (y^3/3 - y)$ is small. The solution eventually becomes periodic as shown in Figure V-10, which consists of almost vertical lines AB, DC and curves BD and CA which are almost portions of the curve $x = y^3/3 - y$. In fact, as $\varepsilon \to 0$, the solution to (60) is given by vertical lines and portions of the curve $x = y^3/3 - y$. The above-described behavior is called relaxation oscillation. The term "almost discontinu-

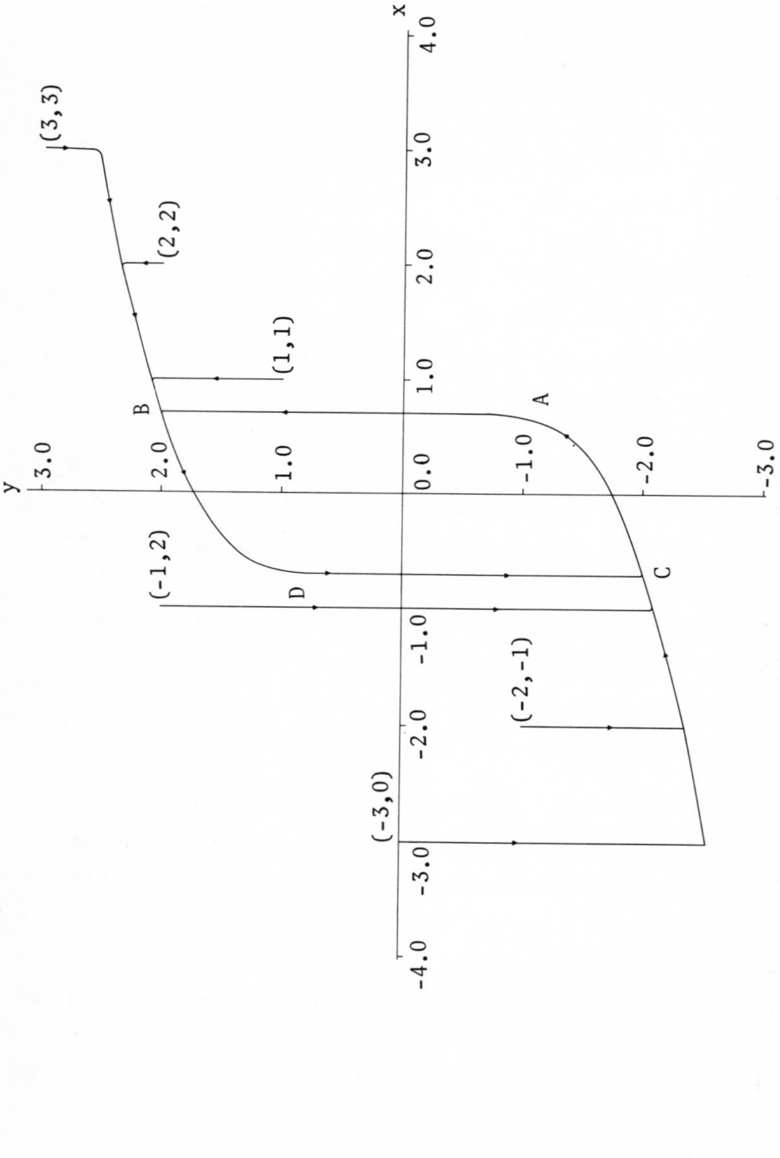

FIGURE V-10: Oscillation for system (60), $\varepsilon = 0.05$.

ous" is used to characterize this oscillation, since the slope of the trajectory for $\varepsilon \neq 0$ changes rather abruptly at the points A and C. It may be observed that, in Figure V-10, the solution moves very rapidly along AB and DC, whereas the solution is moving rather slowly along BD and CA.

The presence of relaxation oscillation has been known since van der Pol, who observed them in electrical circuits. Several authors have since considered the behavior of van der Pol oscillators; in fact, the December 1960 issue of the *IRE Transactions on Circuit Theory* was devoted to studies of van der Pol [2] oscillators. The work of two authors, who have considered the problem of relaxation oscillation, may be mentioned in particular. Dorodnicyn [1] considers various regions in the phase plane and derives an asymptotic series for the solution in each of these regions. Cartwright [1] studies the solution $y(t)$ and considers the solution in various regions of the (t,y)-plane. These methods are of rather limited usefulness, for they are only applicable to the van der Pol oscillator. The more recent method of singular perturbation has much wider applicability and is the subject of the remainder of this section.

Consider the system

$$\begin{aligned} \dot{x} &= f(x,y,t,\varepsilon) \\ \varepsilon\dot{y} &= g(x,y,t,\varepsilon) \quad , \end{aligned} \tag{61}$$

where x,y are n and m vectors, f and g are continuously differentiable functions in each of their arguments, and $\varepsilon << 1$. For $\varepsilon = 0$, the system (61) reduces to

$$\begin{aligned} \dot{x} &= f(x,y,t,0) \\ 0 &= g(x,y,t,0) \quad . \end{aligned} \tag{62}$$

The system (61) is a generalization of the system (60). The methods which determine the behavior of the system (61) from the behavior of the system (62) are called singular perturbation methods. A variety of properties such as the existence of periodic solutions and stability of the singular points of the system (61), may be discussed via these methods. The attractiveness of singular perturbation methods is easily seen by observing that system (61) is of order m+n whereas the system (62) is of order n together with an algebraic side condition.

Problems involving equations of the form (61) arise in a variety of areas. In particular, electrical circuits containing parasitic elements may be described by differential equations of the form (61). However, in general, it is not possible to deduce the behavior of such systems by considering the system without the parasitic elements, *i.e.*, system (62). In fact, it is possible to arrive at incorrect results about system (61), containing parasitic elements, by considering only system (62), the model containing no parasitic elements. The following interesting example, due to Shensa [1], illustrates this point.

Example: Consider the two circuits shown in Figure V-11, where (a) contains the parasitic capacitor ε and (b) has no parasitic capacitor. The i-v characteristic for the diode is shown in Figure V-11(c). The differential equations for the network containing the parasitic element are

$$\frac{di}{dt} = -i - v + E$$

$$\varepsilon \frac{dv}{dt} = i - g(v) \quad .$$

By drawing the load line, as shown in Figure V-11(c), it is

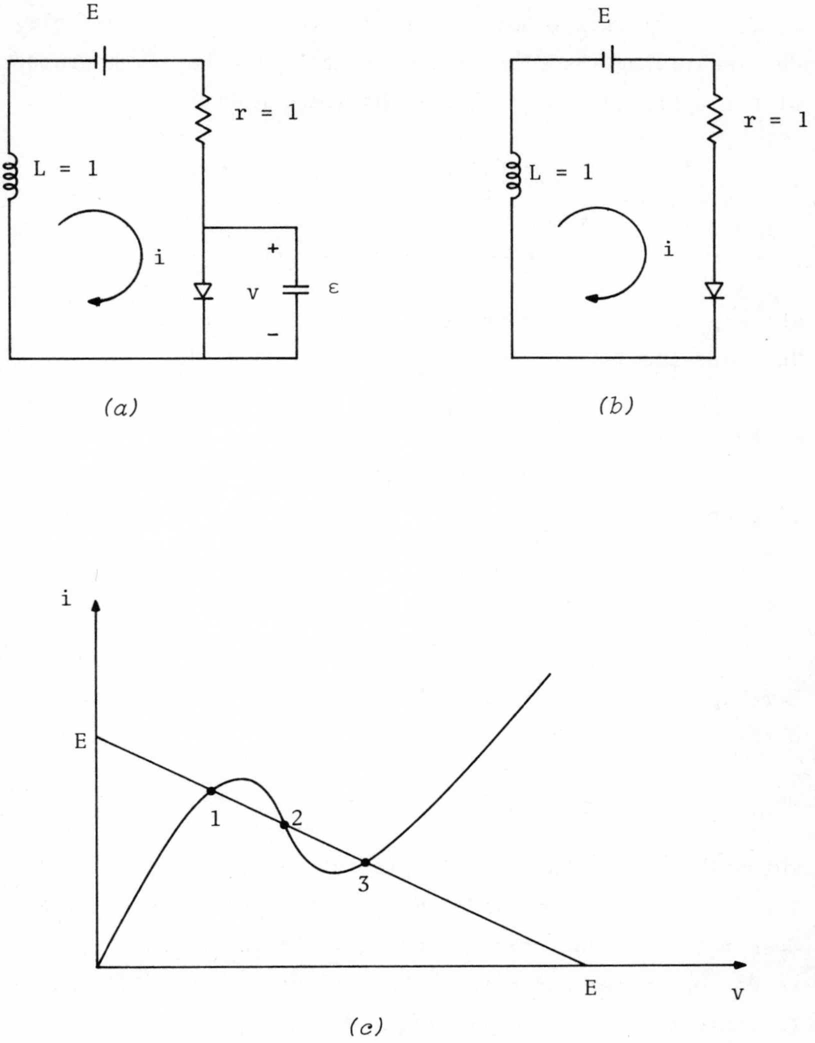

FIGURE V-11: *Electric circuit with parasitic elements.*

easily seen that there are three possible operating points: 1, 2, 3. Operating point 2 is of interest in this example. On linearizing the diode characteristic in the neighborhood of the operating point 2, one obtains

$$\frac{di}{dt} = -i - v + E$$

$$\varepsilon \frac{dv}{dt} = i + g_o v - I_o \quad ,$$

where g_o and I_o are constants. Let us assume that $g_o > 1$. The characteristic polynomial for the system is $\lambda^2 + \lambda(1 - g_o/\varepsilon) + 1/\varepsilon - g_o/\varepsilon$, and, for sufficiently small ε, the operating point is unstable.

The equations for the circuit without the parasitic element are

$$\frac{di}{dt} = -i - v + E$$

$$i - g(v) = 0 \quad .$$

Here again, on linearizing about the operating point 2 one obtains

$$\frac{di}{dt} = i(-1 + 1/g_o) - I_o/g_o + E$$

which shows that the operating point is stable if $g_o > 1$. Thus, in general, the model without the parasitic elements does not yield the correct results. In the following, the conditions under which the behaviors of systems (61) and (62) are similar, are investigated.

Consider the linear system

$$\begin{aligned} \dot{x} &= Ax + By \\ \varepsilon\dot{y} &= Cx + Dy \quad , \end{aligned} \tag{63}$$

and the system corresponding to $\varepsilon = 0$,

$$\begin{aligned} \dot{x} &= Ax + By \\ 0 &= Cx + Dy \quad , \end{aligned} \tag{64}$$

where A and D are square matrices and B and C are compatible matrices. The behavior of the singular point at the origin for system (63) may be deduced from the simpler system (64) by the following theorem due to Shensa [1].

Theorem: Let the eigenvalues of D be in the open left-half plane. Then, if the eigenvalues of $R \triangleq A - BD^{-1}C$ are in the open left-half plane, there exists an $\varepsilon_o > 0$ such that for every $\varepsilon \in (0, \varepsilon_o]$, the equilibrium point at the origin for the system (63) is asymptotically stable.

Proof: It may be observed that the system (64) reduces to

$$\dot{x} = (A - BD^{-1}C)x = Rx \quad ,$$

by using $y = -D^{-1}Cx$. Consider the matrix

$$F_\varepsilon = \begin{bmatrix} A & B \\ C/\varepsilon & D/\varepsilon \end{bmatrix} .$$

If the eigenvalues of F_ε are in the open left-half plane, then the system (63) is asymptotically stable. Let $\varepsilon > 0$, λ_ε be an eigenvalue of F_ε and $\begin{bmatrix} x_\varepsilon \\ y_\varepsilon \end{bmatrix}$ be the eigenvector corresponding to λ_ε. Then,

$$\begin{aligned} Ax_\varepsilon + By_\varepsilon &= \lambda_\varepsilon x_\varepsilon \\ Cx_\varepsilon + Dy_\varepsilon &= \varepsilon\lambda_\varepsilon y_\varepsilon \ . \end{aligned}$$

Several cases arise at this point and are considered next.

If $(D - \varepsilon\lambda_\varepsilon I)^{-1}$ exists, then

$$y_\varepsilon = -(D - \varepsilon\lambda_\varepsilon I)^{-1} C x_\varepsilon ,$$

from which one can define

$$G_\varepsilon x_\varepsilon \triangleq [A-B(D - \varepsilon\lambda_\varepsilon I)^{-1}C]x_\varepsilon = \lambda_\varepsilon x_\varepsilon ,$$

and λ_ε is an eigenvalue of $G_\varepsilon \triangleq A-B(D - \varepsilon\lambda_\varepsilon I)^{-1}C$. If λ_ε is a bounded function of ε, then $\varepsilon\lambda_\varepsilon \to 0$, and $[A-B(D - \varepsilon\lambda_\varepsilon I)^{-1}C] \to [A-BD^{-1}C] = R$ as $\varepsilon \to 0$. Thus λ_ε lies in the open left-half plane for sufficiently small ε. If λ_ε is an unbounded function of ε, then $|\varepsilon\lambda_\varepsilon|$ is a bounded function of ε, as seen from the following. For $|\lambda_\varepsilon|$ sufficiently large, the inverse of the matrix $A - \lambda_\varepsilon I$ exists, so

$$x_\varepsilon = - (A - \lambda_\varepsilon I)^{-1} B y_\varepsilon .$$

Also,

$$\varepsilon\lambda_\varepsilon y_\varepsilon = Cx_\varepsilon + Dy_\varepsilon ,$$

or

$$\begin{aligned} |\varepsilon\lambda_\varepsilon| \, \|y_\varepsilon\| &\leq \|C\| \, \|x_\varepsilon\| + \|D\| \, \|y_\varepsilon\| \\ &\leq [\|C\| \, \|(A - \lambda_\varepsilon I)^{-1}\| \, \|B\| + \|D\|] \, \|y_\varepsilon\| \\ &\leq [\|C\| \, \|B\| + \|D\|] \, \|y_\varepsilon\| \end{aligned}$$

for sufficiently large λ_ε. Thus $|\varepsilon\lambda_\varepsilon|$ is bounded as $\varepsilon \to 0$. Now, λ_ε is an eigenvalue of G_ε; thus $\|G_\varepsilon\|$ is unbounded, which is the same as saying that certain terms of G_ε are unbounded. This is possible only if $\det(D - \varepsilon\lambda_\varepsilon I) \to 0$ as $\varepsilon \to 0$. Therefore, λ_ε is in the open left-half plane for sufficiently small ε.

If $(D - \varepsilon\lambda_\varepsilon I)$ is singular, then $\varepsilon\lambda_\varepsilon$ is an eigenvalue of D; here again λ_ε is in the open left-half plane for sufficiently small ε.

Now there is only a finite number of eigenvalues of F_ε, and an ε_o may be chosen such that all eigenvalues of F_ε are in the open left-half plane for $\varepsilon \in (0, \varepsilon_o]$. Hence, the theorem. ◆

Exercise 9: Find the conditions under which the stability of the singular points of the system (62) implies the stability of the singular points of the system (61).

Exercise 10: If one of the eigenvalues of R is in the right-half plane, show that there exists an ε_o such that for every $\varepsilon \in (0, \varepsilon_o]$ the system (63) is unstable.

Exercise 11: Find the necessary and sufficient conditions for the stability of the second-order system

$$\dot{x} = ax + by$$

$$\varepsilon \dot{y} = cx + dy$$

for $\varepsilon \in (0, \varepsilon_o]$, and compare these conditions with those obtained from the theorem above.

Exercise 12: Find the necessary and sufficient conditions for the stability of the system

$$\dot{x}_1 = a_{11}x_1 + a_{12}x_2 + a_{13}y_1$$

$$\dot{x}_2 = a_{21}x_1 + a_{22}x_2 + a_{23}y_1$$

$$\varepsilon \dot{y}_1 = a_{31}x_1 + a_{32}x_2 + a_{33}y_1$$

for $\varepsilon \in (0, \varepsilon_o]$ and compare these conditions with those obtained from the theorem above.

5. *Other Approximation Methods*

The approximation techniques associated with quasilinear behavior and singular perturbation have been discussed in the last three sections. It has been possible to present a limited number of problems and a limited number of techniques. The literature on approximation methods is so vast that any attempt at completeness of discussion in the present notes would be foolhardy. In the following, several important topics are presented to the reader for his further interest.

The existence of periodic solutions was discussed for the system (11). This discussion may be continued with systems of the form

$$\dot{x} = Ax + f(x,\varepsilon) \tag{23}$$

or

$$\ddot{x} + \omega^2 x = \varepsilon f(x,\dot{x},t,\varepsilon) \tag{21}$$

or

$$\ddot{x} + \omega^2 x = \varepsilon f(x,\dot{x}) \quad . \tag{22}$$

The theorem on page 116 is certainly not applicable to any systems of the form (21), (22), (23). A discussion of the above topics is found in Struble [1] and Cesari [1]. Cesari [1] presents several more sophisticated versions of the above results.

In the development of approximate expressions for the solution of quasilinear systems, second-order autonomous systems are considered in Section 3. Problems described by

$$\ddot{x} + \omega^2 x = \varepsilon f(x,\dot{x},t) \quad ,$$

where $f(x,\dot{x},t)$ is periodic in t, are discussed by Bogoliubov and Mitropolsky [1]. Generalization to higher-order systems have been presented by Butenin [1].

In the context of singular perturbation, the results on existence of periodic solutions are presented by Halanay [1]. Interested readers are also referred to the original papers of Pontryagin [1], Miščenko [1] and Tihonov [1]. Certain applications of singular perturbation problems is also presented by Kokotovic and Sannuti [1].

Recently, Desoer and Shensa [1] have considered the problem of systems containing both large and small parameters, *i.e.*, systems of the form

$$\dot{x} = f_1(x,y,z)$$

$$\varepsilon\dot{y} = f_2(x,y,z)$$

$$\mu\dot{z} = f_3(x,y,z) \quad .$$

These differential systems arise where the system contains both parasitic elements as well as sluggish elements. The stability of the singular points of such a system may be deduced from the consideration of simpler models. For detailed results on such systems, the reader is referred to the paper by Desoer and Shensa [1].

As mentioned earlier, the literature on approximate methods is vast and varied. It has been possible to discuss only a few techniques. These techniques center around the construction of an approximate expression or the investigation of properties of periodicity and stability for the solution of the nonlinear systems in terms of the solution of the systems with known solutions or properties. The interested reader is recommended to the references mentioned above for further study of the subject.

CHAPTER VI

DIGITAL COMPUTER METHODS

1. *Introduction*

It is indeed a rare occasion when a nonlinear problem has a closed-form solution. Chapters II through V have been devoted to the qualitative properties of solutions, such as stability of solutions, existence of periodic solutions, and quantitative methods, such as finding approximate expressions for the solution of nonlinear systems. The inability to find properties of nonlinear systems and the lack of closed-form solutions makes the need for the computation of particular solutions evident. The present chapter is motivated by this need and is devoted primarily to the numerical solution of differential systems. Unlike the methods described earlier, numerical solution of differential systems is of universal applicability: if all else fails, one may fall back on the numerical computation of the solution. However, the discussion of the numerical methods given here, as well as other observations, are limited to first-order systems since the algebra becomes very difficult for higher-order systems.

The numerical computation of a solution on a digital computer is essentially a discrete process. It must also be emphasized that by the use of a digital computer one is not determining a function but the values of a function at a set of isolated points. For example, by the solution of the initial-value problem

$$\dot{y}(t) = Y(y,t) \quad , \quad y(t_o) = y_o \tag{1}$$

is meant the problem of determining a function $y(t)$ such that $y(t_o) = y_o$ and the equation (1) is satisfied identically. By the digital computer solution of the problem is meant the determination of the values of the function $y(\cdot)$ at a given set of points $t_1, t_2, \ldots, t_N$, when $t_o < t_1 < t_2 \ldots < t_N$. Usually, the points t_i are distributed uniformly, *i.e.*, $t_i = t_o + ih$, $i = 1,2,\ldots,N$, and h is a positive constant.

Let $y(\cdot)$ be the true solution of (1) and $\eta(\cdot)$ be the computed solution. The following notation is used:

$$\begin{aligned} y_i &= y(t_i) \quad , \quad \dot{y}_i = Y(y_i,t_i) \quad , \\ \eta_i &= \eta(t_i) \quad , \quad \dot{\eta}_i = Y(\eta_i,t_i) \quad . \end{aligned} \tag{2}$$

It may be observed that the function $\eta(\cdot)$ is defined at the discrete points t_i and $\dot{\eta}_i = Y(\eta_i,t_i)$ is purely for the purposes of notation. It is the objective of a method for the numerical solution of initial-value problems to keep the discretization error

$$y_i - \eta_i \tag{3}$$

small.

Several books which develop the subject in detail have been written on the subject of numerical solution of differential equations. However, the objectives of this chapter are limited to presenting basic notions of numerical solutions rather than enabling the reader to write some of the more sophisticated programs for numerical solutions, or to perform complex error analysis of various numerical methods. This approach is motivated by the fact that in the software package of most modern large-scale digital computers there are differential equation solving routines.

The restricting of the discussion of computer methods to the digital computer is motivated by the following:

(i) the easy accessibility of digital computers,

(ii) the lack of restriction on the type of non-linearity,

(iii) the high degree of accuracy,

(iv) the availability of graphical output via cathode ray tube or plotter.

This is not to imply that analog or hybrid computers may not be more suitable for certain systems; however, in general, digital computers offer greater flexibility in the solution of problems.

The evaluation of a solution of the initial-value problem (1) involves the writing of a program to evaluate the right-hand side of the differential equation, *i.e.*, $Y(y,t)$. The time required to compute the solution depends upon the nature of the differential equation, the computer, and the method of solution. The objective in writing a program for the numerical solution of the initial-value problem is to obtain the value of the solution function at the desired points with maximum accuracy, in minimum time, using minimum computer storage.

The iterative method of Picard provides a convenient starting point for the discussion of digital computer methods. This iterative technique reduces the initial-value problem to the finding of an iterative solution for the integral equation

$$\hat{y}(t) = y_o + \int_{t_o}^{t} Y(\hat{y}(\tau),\tau)d\tau \ . \tag{4}$$

The iterates are used to prove the existence and uniqueness of the solution to the initial-value problem, but these iterates are rarely used in the numerical computation of the solution. However, it is instructive to consider these iterates since they offer insight into the construction of the solution.

There are two types of methods most commonly used for the numerical solution of the initial value problems. They are designated by the names Numerical Integration Methods and Runge-Kutta Type Methods. The basic motivations for these two approaches are distinct.

The Numerical Integration Methods are based upon the fitting of a polynomial approximation to the solution function. This technique is motivated by the fact that a continuous function, defined on a finite interval, may be approximated arbitrarily closely by a suitable polynomial. (For details, see Weierstrass Approximation Theorem, Wilf [1].)

The desire not to evaluate derivatives of $Y(y,t)$ leads to a polynomial approximation of the form

$$\begin{aligned} y(t_o + (n+1)h) &= \sum_{i=0}^{p} a_i \, y(t_o + (n-i)h) \\ &+ h \sum_{i=-1}^{p} b_i \, \dot{y}(t_o + (n-i)h) + T_p \ , \end{aligned} \tag{5}$$

where n and p are integers, $n \geq p$, the a's and b's are constants dependent upon the particular polynomial approximation used, and T_p is the error due to the polynomial approximation of the function $y(\cdot)$. It is interesting to note that the value of the function $y(\cdot)$ at $t_o + (n+1)h$ is approximated in terms of the values of the solution function $y(\cdot)$ at $t_o + (n-i)h$, $i = 0,1,2,\ldots,p$ and its derivatives at $t_o + (n-i)h$, $i = -1,0,1,2,\ldots,p$.

Runge-Kutta type methods are based on Taylor's expansion of the function $y(\cdot)$. The solution function $y(\cdot)$, under suitable conditions, may be expanded into Taylor's series

$$y(t_o+(n+1)h) = y(t_o+nh) + h\dot{y}(t_o+nh) + \frac{h^2}{2!}\ddot{y}(t_o+nh) + \ldots + \frac{h^m}{m!}y^{(m)}(t_o+nh) + T_T \quad , \tag{6}$$

where $T_T = O(h^{m+1})$, $y^{(m)}(t_o+nh) = \left.\frac{d^m y(t)}{dt^m}\right|_{t=t_o+nh}$, and $m \geq 1$. The evaluation of $y(t_o+(n+1)h)$ via Taylor series involves the computation of the derivatives of $Y(y,t)$ for $m \geq 2$. Runge-Kutta type methods remove this difficulty by developing an alternate expression for

$$h\dot{y}(t_o+nh) + \frac{h^2}{2!}\ddot{y}(t_o+nh) + \ldots + \frac{h^m}{m!}y^{(m)}(t_o+nh) \tag{7}$$

which does not involve derivatives of $Y(y,t)$ but agrees with (7) with an error of $O(h^{m+1})$. Runge-Kutta type methods essentially duplicate Taylor's expansion without the disadvantage of evaluating the derivatives of $Y(y,t)$.

The highlights of the three methods mentioned above are presented in the following sections.

2. *Picard's Iterates*

Let us consider the initial-value problem (1). If a function $\hat{y}(t)$ satisfies the integral equation (4), then $\hat{y}(t)$ is a solution to the initial-value problem. This observation follows by differentiating (4) and on noticing that $\hat{y}(t_o) = y_o$. The solution to the integral equation (4) is constructed iteratively by defining the functions

$$
\begin{aligned}
y^0(t) &= y_o \\
y^1(t) &= y_o + \int_{t_o}^{t} Y(y^0(\tau),\tau)\,d\tau \\
y^2(t) &= y_o + \int_{t_o}^{t} Y(y^1(\tau),\tau)\,d\tau \\
&\cdots\cdots \\
y^{i+1}(t) &= y_o + \int_{t_o}^{t} Y(y^i(\tau),\tau)\,d\tau \\
&\cdots\cdots \quad .
\end{aligned}
\tag{8}
$$

The purpose of this section is to show that the iterates (8) are well defined and that

$$\lim_{i \to \infty} y^i(t) = \hat{y}(t) \quad ,$$

is a solution to the integral equation, and thus a solution to the initial-value problem (1). A sufficient set of conditions for this to hold is given by the theorem below.

Definition: Lipschitz Function. Let $Y(y,t)$ be a continuous function on an open region R in the (y,t)-plane such that for every (y_1,t), (y_2,t) in R

$$|Y(y_1,t) - Y(y_2,t)| \le L|y_1 - y_2| \quad , \tag{9}$$

where L is a constant; then the function $Y(y,t)$ is Lipschitz in y on R, and L is known as the Lipschitz constant.

The Lipschitz condition plays an important role in proving properties concerning Picard's iterates. It may be observed that a function $Y(y,t)$, continuous on an open region R, with a continuous partial derivative $\partial Y(y,t)/\partial y$, is Lipschitz in y. It will be an interesting exercise for the reader to prove this observation.

Theorem: A solution to the initial value problem (1) is

$$\lim_{i \to \infty} y^i(t) = \hat{y}(t) \tag{10}$$

provided that

(i) $Y(y,t)$ is continuous on an open region R,

(ii) (y_o,t_o) is in R,

(iii) for every (y_1,t), (y_2,t) in R, $|Y(y_1,t) - Y(y_2,t)| \leq L|y_1-y_2|$, where L is a constant.

Proof: Let R^* be the rectangle

$$|t - t_o| \leq a$$

$$|y - y_o| \leq c$$

lying inside the region R. This is possible for some a and c since the region R is open. Next, consider the function $Y(y,t)$ defined on R^*; it has a maximum M on R^* since $Y(y,t)$ is continuous on R^*. Let b be the minimum of a and $\frac{c}{M}$, and denote the rectangle

$$|t - t_o| \leq b$$

$$|y - y_o| \leq c$$

by $\hat{R}$. The regions R, R^* and $\hat{R}$ are shown in Figure VI-1.

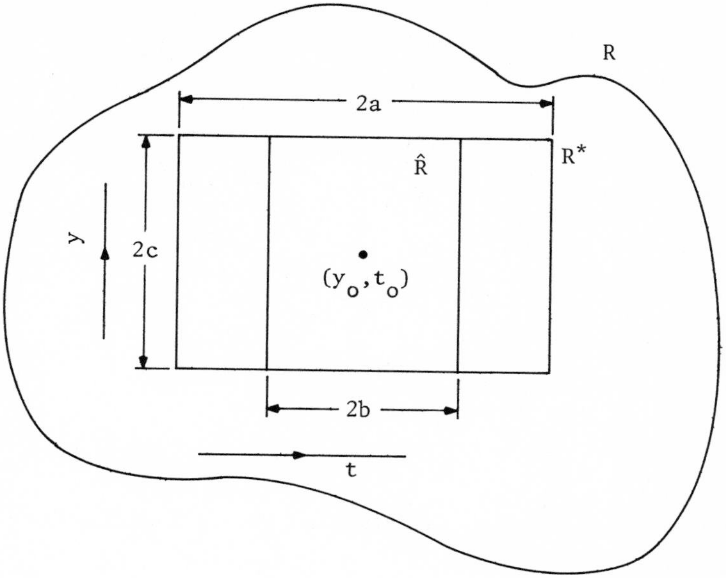

FIGURE VI-1: Region of validity for Picard's iterates.

It is proved in the following that the iterates (8) are well defined on $\hat{R}$, and that the limit (10) exists, and gives a solution to the initial-value problem (1). The proof is given in four parts for better understanding of the properties of the iterates:

(i) The definition of iterates.

Let $|t - t_o| \leq b$; then

$$|y^1(t) - y_o| = |\int_{t_o}^{t} Y(y^0(\tau),\tau)d\tau|$$

$$\leq M|t - t_o|$$

$$\leq Mb$$

$$\leq c.$$

Further, if one assumes $|y^i(t) - y_o| \leq c$, then

$$|y^{i+1}(t) - y_o| \leq |\int_{t_o}^{t} Y(y^i(\tau),\tau)d\tau|$$

$$\leq M|t - t_o|$$

$$\leq Mb$$

$$\leq c$$

Therefore, by induction, the iterates are well defined on $\hat{R}$.

(ii) Boundedness of iterates.

Let $t_o \leq t \leq t_o + b$; then

$$|y^1(t) - y^0(t)| = |\int_{t_o}^{t} Y(y^0(\tau),\tau)d\tau|$$

$$\leq M(t - t_o)$$

Further, if

$$|y^i(t) - y^{i-1}(t)| \leq \frac{ML^{i-1}(t - t_o)^i}{i!} ,$$

then

$$|y^{i+1}(t) - y^i(t)| = \left|\int_{t_o}^{t} [Y(y^i(\tau),\tau) - Y(y^{i-1}(\tau),\tau)]d\tau\right|$$

$$\leq L \int_{t_o}^{t} |y^i(\tau) - y^{i-1}(\tau)|d\tau$$

$$\leq L \frac{ML^{i-1}}{i!} \int_{t_o}^{t} (\tau - t_o)^i d\tau$$

$$\leq \frac{ML^i}{(i+1)!} (t - t_o)^{i+1} \quad .$$

Therefore, by induction, the inequality

$$|y^{i+1}(t) - y^i(t)| \leq \frac{ML^i}{(i+1)!} (t - t_o)^{i+1}$$

holds for $i = 0,1,\ldots$ and $t_o \leq t \leq t_o + b$. A similar argument may be given for $t_o - b \leq t \leq t_o$. Thus, the inequality

$$|y^{i+1}(t) - y^i(t)| \leq \frac{ML^i}{(i+1)!} |t - t_o|^{i+1} \tag{12}$$

holds for $i = 0,1,\ldots,$ and $|t - t_o| \leq b$.

(iii) Convergence of the limit.

Let us consider the series

$$\hat{y}(t) = y_o + \sum_{i=1}^{\infty} (y^i(t) - y^{i-1}(t)). \tag{13}$$

The terms of the series telescope and

$$\lim_{i \to \infty} y^i(t) = \hat{y}(t) \quad .$$

Further, the terms of the series (13) are bounded by the inequality (12) such that

$$|y_o| + \sum_{i=1}^{\infty} |y^i(t) - y^{i-1}(t)| \leq |y_o| + \sum_{i=1}^{\infty} \frac{ML^{i-1}|t - t_o|^i}{i!}$$

$$\leq |y_o| + \frac{M}{L}(e^{bL} - 1) .$$

Thus, the series (13) is uniformly and absolutely convergent and converges to a sum $\hat{y}(t)$. It may be noticed that $\hat{y}(t)$ is continuous.

(iv) Solution to the integral equation.

On taking the limit as $i \to \infty$ of both sides of

$$y^i(t) = y_o + \int_{t_o}^{t} Y(y^{i-1}(\tau),\tau)d\tau ,$$

it follows that $\hat{y}(t)$ is a solution to the integral equation (4). The interchange of the order of the limit and the integration, *i.e.*,

$$\lim_{i \to \infty} \int_{t_o}^{t} Y(y^{i-1}(\tau),\tau)d\tau$$

$$= \int_{t_o}^{t} \lim_{i \to \infty} Y(y^{i-1}(\tau),\tau)d\tau ,$$

is justifiable because of the inequality

$$\left| \int_{t_o}^{t} (Y(\hat{y}(\tau),\tau) - Y(y^{i-1}(\tau),\tau))d\tau \right|$$

$$\leq L \varepsilon_i |t - t_o| ,$$

where

$$\varepsilon_i = |\hat{y}(\tau) - y^{i-1}(\tau)|,$$

$\varepsilon_i \to 0$ as $i \to \infty$, and ε_i is independent of τ.

The arguments (i)-(iv) above lead to the equalities

$$\lim_{i \to \infty} y^i(t) = \hat{y}(t) \quad ,$$

$$\hat{y}(t) = y_0 + \int_{t_0}^{t} Y(\hat{y}(\tau),\tau)d\tau \quad ,$$

i.e., $\hat{y}(t)$ gives a solution to the initial value problem.◆

Example: Consider the initial-value problem

$$\dot{y} = -y, \quad y(t_0) = y_0 \quad . \tag{14}$$

The iterates are

$$y^0(t) = y_0$$

$$y^1(t) = y_0 - y_0(t-t_0)$$

$$y^2(t) = y_0 - y_0(t-t_0) + y_0 \frac{(t-t_0)^2}{2!}$$

$$y^i(t) = y_0 - y_0(t-t_0)+\ldots+(-1)^i y_0 \frac{(t-t_0)^i}{i!} \quad .$$

The limit of $y^i(t)$ as $i \to \infty$ is the series

$$y_0 - y_0(t-t_0)+\ldots+(-1)^i y_0 \frac{(t-t_0)^i}{i!} + \ldots ,$$

which is the same as

$$y_0 e^{-(t-t_0)} \quad ,$$

the correct solution to the initial-value problem.

The iterates y^0, y^1, y^2, y^3 and y^4 together with the exact solution y(t) are shown in Figure VI-2 for the initial value problem (14) with $y(0) = y_0 = 1$, and $0 \leq t \leq 1$.

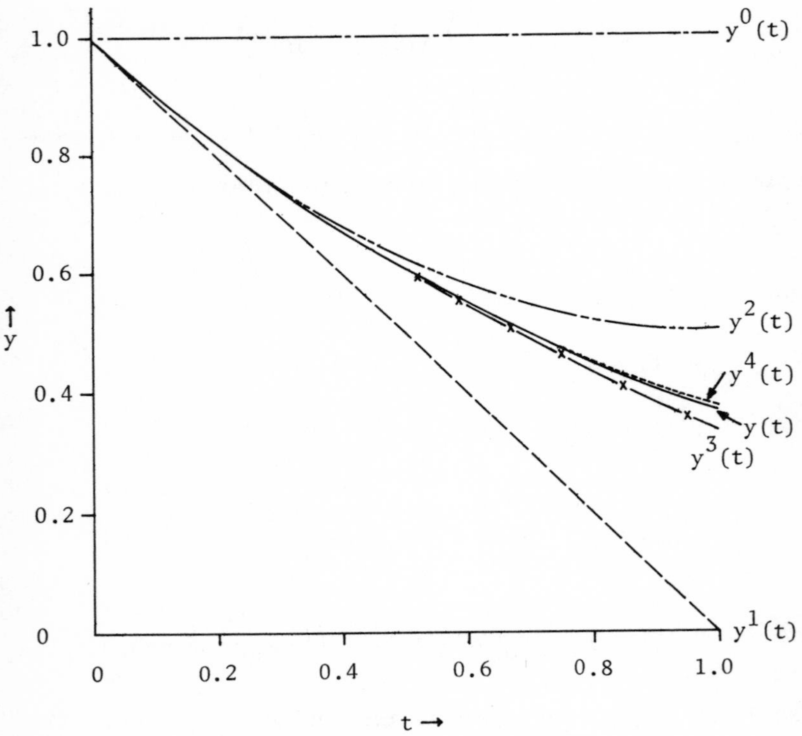

FIGURE VI-2: Picard's iterates for $\dot{y} = -y$, $y(0) = 1$.

The iterates above certainly provide an insight into the construction of the solution. However, they are not useful from the viewpoint of finding numerical solutions. It may be emphasized that the procedure above for the construction of the solution holds for every t, $|t-t_0| \leq b$. This is in contrast to the following methods (Numerical Integration Methods and Runge-Kutta type methods) where the solution is determined only at a discrete set of points, $t_0 + ih$, $h > 0$, $i = 1,2,\ldots,N$.

Exercise 1: Show that the conditions of the theorem above are sufficient for:

(i) the uniqueness of the solution to the initial-value problem (1),

(ii) the continuity of the solution $y(t) = y(t,y_0,t_0)$ to the initial-value problem (1) with respect to the initial condition y_0.

Exercise 2: Modify the proof above for the existence of a solution for the initial-value problem

$$\dot{y}(t) = Y(y,t) \ , \quad y(t_0) = y_0 \ ,$$

where y is an n-vector.

Exercise 3: Give a series solution to the initial-value problem

$$\dot{y} = A(t)y \ , \qquad y(t_0) = y_0 \ , \tag{15}$$

where y is an n-vector.

It must be emphasized that the continuity of the function Y(y,t) is not a necessary condition, whereas the Lipschitz condition, or a condition like the Lipschitz condition, is necessary for the existence and uniqueness of the solution to the initial-value problem. These observations are illustrated by the following examples.

Example: Consider the system

$$\begin{aligned} \dot{y} &= y(1 - 2t) \quad , \quad t \geq 0 \\ &= y(2t - 1) \quad , \quad t < 0 \quad , \\ y(0) &= 1 \quad . \end{aligned} \tag{16}$$

The right-hand side of (16) is discontinuous at t = 0. However,

$$\begin{aligned} y &= e^{t-t^2} \quad , \quad t \geq 0 \\ &= e^{t^2-t} \quad , \quad t \leq 0 \end{aligned}$$

is the unique solution.

Example: The system

$$\dot{y} = \sqrt{|y|} \quad , \quad y(0) = 0$$

admits of the solutions

$$y(t) = 0$$

and

$$\begin{aligned} y(t) &= \frac{1}{4} t^2 \quad , \quad t \geq 0 \\ &= -\frac{1}{4} t^2 \quad , \quad t \leq 0 \quad . \end{aligned}$$

Here Y(y,t) is not Lipschitz at y = 0.

For further discussion of the problems of existence and of uniqueness of solutions, the interested reader may consult Wilf [1], Ince [1] and Coddington and Levinson [1].

3. Numerical Integration Methods

The Weierstrass Approximation Theorem provides the basic motivation for a large number of numerical techniques and, in particular, for numerical integration methods. The polynomial approximation takes the form

$$y(t_0 + (n+1)h) = \sum_{i=0}^{p} a_i \, y(t_0 + (n-i)h) + h \sum_{i=-1}^{p} b_i \, \dot{y}(t_0 + (n-i)h) + T_p \, , \qquad (5)$$

where

p and n are integers, $n \geq p$,

the a_i's and b_i's are constants determined by the polynomial approximation, and

T_p is the error due to the polynomial approximation.

On neglecting the error T_p, the relationship (5) becomes

$$y(t_0 + (n+1)h) \approx \sum_{i=0}^{p} a_i \, y(t_0 + (n-i)h) + h \sum_{i=-1}^{p} b_i \, \dot{y}(t_0 + (n-i)h) \qquad (17)$$

or

$$\eta_{n+1} = \sum_{i=0}^{p} a_i \, \eta_{n-i} + h \sum_{i=-1}^{p} b_i \, \dot{\eta}_{n-i} \; . \qquad (18)$$

A formula of the form (18), which permits recursive evaluation of the solution function, is called a numerical integration formula.

The case p = 0.

In order to make the method more understandable for the reader, the case p = 0 is discussed before presenting the details of the general method (5). With p = 0, (5) reduces to

$$y(t_0 + (n+1)h) = a_0\, y(t_0 + nh) + hb_{-1}\, \dot{y}(t_0 + (n+1)h) + hb_0\, \dot{y}(t_0 + nh) + T_p \; . \tag{19}$$

On neglecting T_p, the polynomial approximation becomes

$$y(t_0 + (n+1)h) \approx a_0\, y(t_0 + nh) + hb_{-1}\, \dot{y}(t_0 + (n+1)h) + hb_0\, \dot{y}(t + nh) \; . \tag{20}$$

Thus, the value of the solution function at $t_0 + (n+1)h$ is approximated in terms of the values of the solution function at $t_0 + nh$, and the values of the derivatives at $t_0 + (n+1)h$ and $t_0 + nh$. The neglected error is called the "local truncation error," and it arises, in the present case, from the polynomial approximation of the solution function. The adjective "local" implies that the error occurs at this particular evaluation of the function. Truncation error tends to accumulate as the solution function is evaluated for more and more points since approximate values of the solution function, or its derivative, may be used in these successive computations. The approximate equality (20) may be written as the equality

$$\eta_{n+1} = a_0\, \eta_n + hb_{-1}\, \dot{\eta}_{n+1} + hb_0\, \dot{\eta}_n \; . \tag{21}$$

In any computer, the computation is carried out with a finite number of digits, and this introduces round-off error. The equation (21), in fact, becomes

$$\eta_{n+1} = a_0 \eta_n + hb_{-1} \dot{\eta}_{n+1} + hb_0 \dot{\eta}_n + R \quad , \tag{22}$$

where R is the local round-off error. Again the word "local" refers to the particular step at which the error occurs. As in the case of truncation errors, the round-off errors accumulate as the solution is computed for more and more points. The magnitude of local round-off error depends upon the type of arithmetic used, floating point or fixed point, and the number of bits used to express each word. In present-day general-purpose computers, where a number is specified by a large number of bits, the round-off error is far less than the truncation error. Analysis of the local truncation and round-off errors, and the discussion of the accumulation, as well as propagation, of these errors are beyond the scope of these *Notes*. The interested reader is recommended to Henrici [1] and Ralston [1] for a discussion of these topics.

There are three constants, a_0, b_{-1}, and b_0, left unspecified in (21). These constants may be chosen to make the formula (21) exact for polynomials of degrees 0, 1, and 2. Let us consider the case where the constants a_0, b_{-1} and b_0 are chosen to make the formula (21) exact for polynomials of degree 0 and 1. The conditions are derived by considering the polynomials t^0 and t^1:

for $y(t) = t^0$,

$$1 = a_0 , \tag{23}$$

for $y(t) = t$,

$$t_o + (n+1)h = a_0(t_o+nh) + h(b_0+b_{-1}) \ . \tag{24}$$

On combining (23) and (24) one obtains

$$a_0 = 1 \ ,$$

$$b_0 + b_{-1} = 1 \ , \tag{25}$$

with

$$b_{-1} = \text{arbitrary constant.}$$

The equality (20) becomes

$$y(t_0 + (n+1)h) \approx y(t_0 + nh) + h(1 - b_{-1})\,\dot{y}(t_0 + nh) + hb_{-1}\,\dot{y}(t_0 + (n+1)h) \ , \tag{26}$$

or

$$\eta_{n+1} = \eta_n + h(1 - b_{-1})\,\dot{\eta}_n + hb_{-1}\,\dot{\eta}_{n+1} \ . \tag{27}$$

If $b_{-1} = 0$, (26) and (27) reduce to

$$y(t_0 + (n+1)h) \approx y(t_0 + nh) + h\dot{y}(t_0 + nh) \tag{28}$$

and

$$\eta_{n+1} = \eta_n + h\,\dot{\eta}_n \ , \tag{29}$$

respectively. Equation (29), known as Euler's method, is the simplest example of an integration formula. Euler's method is exact where $y(t)$ is a polynomial of degree ≤ 1.

Next, let us consider the case where the constants a_0, b_{-1} and b_0 are determined to make the formula (18) exact for polynomials of degrees 0, 1, and 2. The conditions on a_0, b_{-1}, and b_0 are derived by considering the polynomials t^0, t^1, t^2 as follows:

for $y(t) = t^0$,

$$1 = a_0 \ , \tag{30}$$

for $y(t) = t^1$,

$$t_o + (n+1)h = a_0(t_o+nh) + h(b_0+b_{-1}) \quad , \qquad (31)$$

for $y(t) = t^2$,

$$(t_o + (n+1)h)^2 = a_0(t_o+nh)^2 + 2b_0\, h(t_o+nh)$$

$$+ 2b_{-1}\, h(t_o+(n+1)h) \quad . \qquad (32)$$

On simplification of (30), (31) and (32), the conditions on a_0, b_{-1}, b_0, are

$$\begin{aligned} a_0 &= 1 \quad , \\ b_0 + b_{-1} &= 1 \quad , \\ 2b_{-1} &= 1 \quad . \end{aligned} \qquad (33)$$

On solving (33), one obtains

$$\begin{aligned} a_0 &= 1 \quad , \\ b_0 &= \frac{1}{2} \quad , \\ b_{-1} &= \frac{1}{2} \quad . \end{aligned} \qquad (34)$$

Thus, (20) becomes

$$y(t_o + (n+1)h) \approx y(t_o + nh) + \frac{h}{2}(\dot{y}(t_o + nh)$$

$$+ \dot{y}(t_o + (n+1)h)), \qquad (35)$$

and the equality is exact if y(t) is polynomials of degree ≤ 2. The corresponding integration formula is

$$\eta_{n+1} = \eta_n + \frac{h}{2}(\dot{\eta}_{n+1} + \dot{\eta}_n) \quad . \qquad (36)$$

Equation (36) is known as the modified Euler's method. Equation (29) belongs to the class of integration formulae called "forward integration formulae," whereas (36) belongs to the class called "iterative integration formulae." The names are descriptive of the procedures involved in the use of these formulae. Equation (27) is called a forward integration formula, since previously computed or given values are used in the computation. In this case, η_{n+1} is computed in terms of η_n and $\dot{\eta}_n$. The name "iterative integration formula," for (36), arises from the fact that η_{n+1} is computed in terms of η_n, $\dot{\eta}_n$ and the still not available $\dot{\eta}_{n+1} = Y(\eta_{n+1}, t_{n+1})$. Iterative integration formulae arise when $b_{-1} \neq 0$, and are used in an iterative manner in the evaluation of the solution function. By "iterative use" is meant that an estimate of η_{n+1} is made by some other means, say a forward integration formula, and this estimate is used to improve η_{n+1} by using the iterative integration formula. This procedure is known as "predicting" and "correcting," and is presented later.

Euler's method and the modified Euler's method are of order 1 and 2, respectively. "Order" refers to highest degree polynomial for which the formula is exact.

A simplification in the procedure above, for the determination of the conditions on the constants a_0, b_{-1}, b_0, is possible by assuming

$$h = 1$$

and

$$t_0 + nh = 0 \quad , \tag{37}$$

as seen in the following exercise.

Exercise 4: Show that there is no loss of generality by assuming (37) in the determination of the equations for

a_0, b_{-1}, and b_0.

The general case.

The discussion of the general case follows along the lines of the Euler's methods, the simplest of the numerical integration methods. In the general case, the solution $y(t_0 + (n+1)h)$ is computed in terms of p previously computed solution points, $y(t_0 + (n-i)h)$, $i = 0,\ldots,p$, and $p+1$ derivatives of the solution, $\dot{y}(t_0 + (n-i)h)$, $i = -1,0,\ldots,p$. The integration formula is called an iterative integration formula if $b_{-1} \neq 0$, or a forward integration formula if $b_{-1} = 0$.

The coefficients in (18) may be chosen to make the difference equation exact for polynomials of degree $\leq m$, where m is some positive integer. The result of Exercise 4 may be extended to the general case, and the coefficients may be evaluated by assuming $t_0 + nh = 0$ and $h = 1$.

On considering the functions $t^0, t^1, \ldots, t^m$, the equations for the coefficient a's and b's are:

for $y(t) = t^0$,

$$1 = \sum_{i=0}^{p} a_i \quad ,$$

for $y(t) = t^1$,

$$1 = -\sum_{i=0}^{p} i\, a_i + \sum_{i=-1}^{p} b_i \quad , \tag{38}$$

for $y(t) = t^j$,

$$1 = \sum_{i=0}^{p} (-i)^j\, a_i + j \sum_{i=-1}^{p} (-i)^{j-1}\, b_i \; ,$$

$$j = 2,\ldots,m.$$

In the conditions (38), the number of equations is m+1 and the number of variables is 2p + 3.

If $p \geq 1$, an immediate difficulty arises. The value of the function at $t_0 + ih$, $i = 0,\ldots,p$ must be known, but the initial-value problem gives only the value of the function at t_0. Therefore, in the use of numerical integration methods where $p \geq 1$, some auxiliary technique must be used to obtain these values. The methods of the following section, Runge-Kutta type methods, are normally used to obtain these starting values. Thus, numerical integration methods are, in general, used in conjunction with an auxiliary method.

The highest-degree polynomial for which the integration formula is exact gives the order of the formula. The highest order that may be achieved with the formula (18) is $m \leq 2p+2$. In certain integration formulae, conditions besides (38) are added. For example, the constant b_{-1} is set to be zero for forward integration formulae. In addition, other a's and b's also may be specified in order to achieve certain properties of the integration formula. For example, in a certain class of integration formulae, one sets

$$a_0 = 1 \quad , \quad b_{-1} = 0 ,$$

and

$$a_i = 0 \quad \text{for} \quad i \neq 0 \quad .$$

For p = 0, the resulting formula is exact for polynomials of degree 1, and is

$$\eta_{n+1} = \eta_n + h \, \dot{\eta}_n \quad ; \tag{39}$$

for p = 1, the resulting formula is exact for polynomials of degree 2, and is

$$\eta_{n+1} = \eta_n + \frac{h}{2}\,[3\dot{\eta}_n - \dot{\eta}_{n-1}] \ ; \tag{40}$$

and so on.

Example: The solution of the initial-value problem

$$\dot{y} = -y \ , \quad y(0) = 1 \ ,$$

with h = 0.1, using Euler's method is shown in Figure VI-3. The exact solution, $y(t) = e^{-t}$, is also given in the

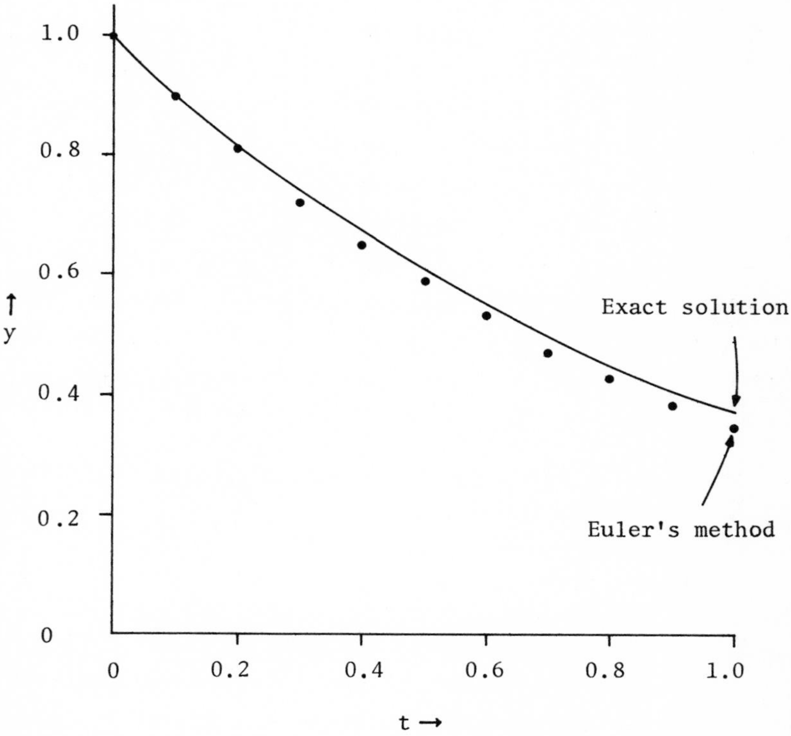

FIGURE VI-3: Solution by Euler's method.

figure to provide a comparison. Euler's method is illustrative of forward integration formulae; however, its use in accurate work is not recommended. Table VI.1 shows the computed and exact values. The computation was performed on a Control Data Corporation 6600 computer.

Table VI.1

Time t	Solution by Euler's Method	Exact Solution
0.0	1.00000	1.00000
0.1	0.90000	0.90484
0.2	0.81000	0.81873
0.3	0.72900	0.74082
0.4	0.65610	0.67032
0.5	0.59049	0.60653
0.6	0.53144	0.54881
0.7	0.47830	0.49658
0.8	0.43047	0.44933
0.9	0.38742	0.40657
1.0	0.34868	0.36788

Exercise 5: Solve the initial-value problem

$$\dot{y} = y \quad , \quad y(0) = 1$$

by Euler's method.

Predictor-corrector methods.

Two types of integration formulae have been discussed, the iterative integration formula and the forward integration formula. Two such formulae are

$$\eta_{n+1} = \eta_n + \frac{h}{2} (\dot{\eta}_{n+1} + \dot{\eta}_n) \ , \qquad (36)$$

$$\eta_{n+1} = \eta_n + \frac{h}{2}(3\dot{\eta}_n - \dot{\eta}_{n-1}) . \tag{40}$$

Equation (36) is an iterative integration formula which is exact for polynomials of degree ≤ 2. Equation (40) is a forward integration formula which is also exact for polynomials of degree ≤ 2. It may be said as a general rule that, among formulae of the same order, the iterative formula is more accurate than the forward integration formula. Further, the added difficulty of iterating is outweighed by the additional accuracy obtained by using an iterative formula.

The "Predictor-Corrector Method" arises from the fact that a forward integration formula is used for "predicting" a solution, and the iterative formula is used for "correcting" this estimate. Let us denote the estimated value of η_{n+1}, obtained by using the predictor, by $\eta_{n+1}^{(0)}$ and the successive values obtained by iteration by $\eta_{n+1}^{(1)}, \eta_{n+1}^{(2)} \ldots$. A predictor-corrector combination is as follows:

$$\text{Predictor:} \quad \eta_{n+1}^{(0)} = \eta_n + \frac{h}{2}(3\dot{\eta}_n - \dot{\eta}_{n-1}) \tag{41}$$

$$\text{Corrector:} \quad \eta_{n+1}^{(j+1)} = \eta_n + \frac{h}{2}(\dot{\eta}_{n+1}^{(j)} + \dot{\eta}_n) , \tag{42}$$

where

$$\dot{\eta}_{n+1}^{(j)} = Y(\eta_{n+1}^{(j)}, t_{n+1}) \text{ and } j = 0,1,\ldots \quad .$$

The superscript on η corresponds to the estimated values of η obtained by using the corrector j times. In view of the iterative process given by the predictor-corrector method, the question of convergence of the iterative process immediately arises.

Let us consider the general relationship for the corrector and the successive iterations obtained by using this relationship. Relationship (18) may be used iteratively as

$$\eta_{n+1}^{(j+1)} = \sum_{i=0}^{p} (a_i \eta_{n-i} + hb_i \dot{\eta}_{n-i}) + hb_{-1} \dot{\eta}_{n+1}^{(j)} . \qquad (43)$$

The value given by the iterative integration formula satisfies the equality

$$\eta_{n+1} = \sum_{i=0}^{p} (a_i \eta_{n-i} + hb_i \dot{\eta}_{n-i}) + hb_{-1} \dot{\eta}_{n+1} . \qquad (44)$$

On subtracting (44) from (43), one obtains

$$\begin{aligned} \eta_{n+1}^{(j+1)} - \eta_{n+1} &= hb_{-1}(\dot{\eta}_{n+1}^{(j)} - \dot{\eta}_{n+1}) \\ &= hb_{-1}[Y(\eta_{n+1}^{(j)}, t_{n+1}) - Y(\eta_{n+1}, t_{n+1})] . \end{aligned} \qquad (45)$$

The right-hand side of (45) may be estimated by using the Lipschitz condition, giving

$$|\eta_{n+1}^{(j+1)} - \eta_{n+1}| \le (h|b_{-1}|L)|\eta_{n+1}^{(j)} - \eta_{n+1}| , \qquad (46)$$

where L is the Lipschitz constant. Successive use of this inequality leads to

$$|\eta_{n+1}^{(j+1)} - \eta_{n+1}| \le (h|b_{-1}|L)^{(j+1)}|\eta_{n+1}^{(0)} - \eta_{n+1}| . \qquad (47)$$

Therefore, a sufficient condition for convergence is

$$|hb_{-1} L| < 1 . \qquad (48)$$

The rate of convergence is determined by the magnitude of $|hb_{-1} L|$; thus, for rapid convergence, $|hb_{-1} L| \ll 1$ is desirable. One possible solution to this convergence problem is the choice of $h \ll 1$. However, making $h \ll 1$ is not desirable, since one is interested in making the total time of computation small. The value of h is usually arrived at by a compromise of several considerations, including computation time and rapid convergence. The most time-consuming portion of the calculation is the evaluation of $\dot{\eta}$ from η; *i.e.*, the evaluation of $Y(\eta,t)$. In the comparison of various methods, the number of iterations to achieve a given accuracy may be used as a good measure of efficiency. The number of iterations, in general, depends upon the accuracy of the initial guess.

The method most often used in terminating the iterative process is the difference between two successive iterates. For example, if

$$|\eta_{n+1}^{(j+1)} - \eta_{n+1}^{(j)}| \leq \varepsilon \quad , \tag{49}$$

where ε is a preassigned small number, the iterative process is terminated.

Now, going back to equations (41) and (42), it may be remarked that it is desirable to use predictors and correctors of the same order. The availability of the large variety of predictors and correctors makes the choice of a suitable algorithm necessary. A discussion of several predictor-corrector methods, together with several examples, is given by Ralston [1]. The use of the fourth-order predictor-corrector method is more common, and is found to be quite adequate for most problems.

Example: The solution of the initial-value problem

$$\dot{y} = -y \quad , \quad y(0) = 1 \quad ,$$

with h = 0.1, using the predictor-corrector combination (41) and (42) is shown in Table VI.2. The value of the solution at t = 0.1 is needed in order to use the predictor. The value was assumed to be $e^{-0.1}$ for the present computation. It must be strongly emphasized that this assumption is not possible in general, where the solution is not known. The manner in which this difficulty may be overcome is discussed in the next section. The error criterion

$$|\eta_n^{(j+1)} - \eta_n^{(j)}| \leq 10^{-4}$$

was used for the termination of the corrector iterative process. The solution of the problem by this predictor-corrector combination is a considerable improvement over the solution by Euler's method.

Table VI.2

Time t				
0.0	1.00000	Initial condition		Starting Values
0.1	0.90484	Starting value assumed $e^{-0.1}$		
	Predicted Value $\eta^{(0)}$	Corrected Value $\eta^{(1)}$	Corrected Value $\eta^{(2)}$	Exact Solution
0.2	0.81911	0.81864	0.81866	0.81873
0.3	0.74110	0.74067	0.74070	0.74082
0.4	0.67052	0.67013	0.67015	0.67032
0.5	0.60667	0.60631	0.60633	0.60653
0.6	0.54889	0.54857	0.54859	0.54881
0.7	0.49661	0.49633	0.49634	0.49658
0.8	0.44932	0.44906	0.44907	0.44933
0.9	0.40653	0.40629	0.40630	0.40657
1.0	0.36781	0.36760	0.36761	0.36788

Exercise 6: Solve the initial-value problem

$$\dot{y} = y \quad , \quad y(0) = 1$$

by the predictor-corrector combination (40) and (36) with $h = 0.1$, $y(0.1) = e^{0.1}$.

4. *Runge-Kutta Type Methods*

The Taylor's expansion of a function $y(t)$ may be expressed as

$$y(t_o + (n+1)h) = y(t_o+nh) + h\dot{y}(t_o+nh) + \frac{h^2}{2!}\ddot{y}(t_o+nh)+\ldots$$
$$+ \frac{h^m}{m!} y^{(m)}(t_o+nh) + T_T \ , \qquad (6)$$

where m is an integer ≥ 1 and $T_T = O(h^{m+1})$. The value of the function at $t_o + (n+1)h$ is approximated in terms of the value of the function and its derivatives at $t_o + nh$. The need to compute derivatives of $Y(y,t)$ for $m \geq 2$ makes Taylor's expansion unsuitable for the numerical solution of differential equations. Runge-Kutta type methods duplicate the Taylor's expansion in such a manner that no derivatives of $Y(y,t)$ are needed in the computation, and the error still remains $O(h^{m+1})$. The actual magnitude of the error is different, but the order of the error is unchanged. This is accomplished by replacing the evaluation of the derivatives of $Y(y,t)$ by the repeated evaluation of $Y(y,t)$.

The case m = 2.

The Runge-Kutta type method in its generality involves complicated expressions and one easily loses sight of the basic ideas motivating the method. In order to develop the basic ideas without the cumbersome formulae, the simplest case is discussed in detail followed by the general formulation of the method. The difficulty of the evaluation of the derivative of $Y(y,t)$ in Taylor's expansion first arises if $m = 2$, when $\ddot{y}(t_o + nh)$ is needed to make the error $O(h^3)$. Thus, the simplest case of the Runge-Kutta type method corresponds to $m = 2$. For the sake of simplicity, the notation

$$t_o + ih = t_i$$
$$y(t_i) = y_i$$

is used. The notation is repeated here for emphasis.

The Taylor's expansion for the case $m = 2$ is

$$y(t_{n+1}) = y(t_n) + h\dot{y}(t_n) + \frac{h^2}{2!}\ddot{y}(t_n) + O(h^3) \tag{50}$$

or

$$y(t_{n+1}) - y(t_n) = h\dot{y}(t_n) + \frac{h^2}{2!}\ddot{y}(t_n) + O(h^3). \tag{51}$$

Let us express $\ddot{y}(t_n)$ in a more suitable form by the following series of equalities:

$$\begin{aligned}\ddot{y}(t_n) &= \frac{d}{dt}(\dot{y}(t))\Big|_{t=t_n} \\ &= \frac{d}{dt}(Y(y(t),t))\Big|_{t=t_n} \\ &= \left(\frac{\partial Y}{\partial y}Y + \frac{\partial Y}{\partial t}\right)\Big|_{t=t_n} \\ &= Y_y(y_n,t_n)\,Y(y_n,t_n) + Y_t(y_n,t_n)\,. \end{aligned} \tag{52}$$

Thus, (51) may be written as

$$y(t_{n+1}) - y(t_n) = hY(y_n,t_n) + \frac{h^2}{2} Y_y(y_n,t_n)Y(y_n,t_n)$$
$$+ \frac{h^2}{2} Y_t(y_n,t_n) + O(h^3) \quad . \qquad (53)$$

The purpose of the Runge-Kutta type method is to develop an expression for

$$hY(y_n,t_n) + \frac{h^2}{2} Y_y(y_n,t_n)Y(y_n,t_n) + \frac{h^2}{2} Y_t(y_n,t_n) \qquad (54)$$

which does not involve the derivative of $Y(y,t)$ but differs from it with an error of $O(h^3)$. Let us consider the function

$$h\ a_1\ Y(y_n,t_n) + h\ a_2\ Y(y_n + \beta_{21}\ h\ Y(y_n,t_n), t_n + \alpha_2\ h), \qquad (55)$$

where a_1, a_2, α_2 and β_{21} are constants. The particular choice of subscripts on the constants α and β will become more obvious later. It may be observed that (55) consists in the evaluation of the function $Y(y,t)$ at

$$(y_n,t_n)$$

and

$$(y_n + \beta_{21}\ h\ Y(y_n,t_n),\ t_n + \alpha_2\ h) \quad .$$

The important thing to be emphasized is that the arguments for the second evaluation of the function $Y(y,t)$ depend upon $Y(y_n,t_n)$. On expanding the second term about the point (y_n,t_n), (55) becomes

$$h\ a_1\ Y(y_n,t_n) + h\ a_2\ Y(y_n,t_n) + h^2\ a_2\ \beta_{21}\ Y_y(y_n,t_n)Y(y_n,t_n)$$
$$+ h^2\ a_2\ \alpha_2\ Y_t(y_n,t_n) + O(h^3) \ ,$$

or

$$h(a_1+a_2)\ Y(y_n,t_n) + h\ a_2\ \beta_{21}\ Y_y(y_n,t_n)\ Y(y_n,t_n)$$

$$+ h^2\ a_2\ \alpha_2\ Y_t(y_n,t_n) + O(h^3)\ . \qquad (56)$$

The term-by-term comparison of the expressions (53) and (56) yield:

$$a_1 + a_2 = 1\ ,$$

$$a_2\ \beta_{21} = \frac{1}{2}\ , \qquad (57)$$

$$a_2\ \alpha_2 = \frac{1}{2}\ .$$

By this procedure, the constants for the second-order Runge-Kutta type method have been determined. The order of the Runge-Kutta type method refers to the highest power of h for which the two expressions, (53) and (56), agree. Thus, there are three equations to determine four parameters. The choice of $a_2 \neq 0$ as a parameter gives the solution to (57) as

$$a_1 = 1 - a_2\ ,$$

$$\beta_2 = \frac{1}{2a_2}\ , \qquad (58)$$

$$\alpha_2 = \frac{1}{2a_2}\ .$$

In terms of the parameter $a_2 \neq 0$, (55) becomes

$$h(1-a_2)Y(y_n,t_n) + h\ a_2\ Y(y_n + \frac{h}{2a_2}\ Y(y_n,t_n),t_n + \frac{h}{2a_2})\ ,$$

and the terms in Taylor's expansion (53) may be replaced to give

$$y(t_{n+1}) = y(t_n) + h(1 - a_2)\, Y(y_n,t_n) + h\, a_2\, Y(y_n + \frac{h}{2a_2} Y(y_n,t_n), t_n + \frac{h}{2a_2}) + T_R\ , \tag{59}$$

where $T_R = O(h^3)$. On neglecting T_R, the relationship (59) gives

$$y(t_{n+1}) \approx y(t_n) + h(1 - a_2)\, Y(y_n,t_n) + h\, a_2\, Y(y_n + \frac{h}{2a_2} Y(y_n,t_n), t_n + \frac{h}{2a_2})\ , \tag{60}$$

and the difference equation for the computation of the solution function is

$$\eta_{n+1} = \eta_n + h(1-a_2)\, \dot{\eta}_n + h\, a_2\, Y(\eta_n + \frac{h}{2a_2} \dot{\eta}_n, t_n + \frac{h}{2a_2})\ . \tag{61}$$

Some particular cases of this formula are:

for

$$a_2 = \frac{1}{2}\ ,$$

$$\eta_{n+1} = \eta_n + \frac{h}{2} \dot{\eta}_n + \frac{h}{2} Y(\eta_n + h\, \dot{\eta}_n, t_n + h); \tag{62}$$

for

$$a_2 = 1\ ,$$

$$\eta_{n+1} = \eta_n + h\, Y(\eta_n + \frac{h}{2} \dot{\eta}_n, t_n + \frac{h}{2})\ . \tag{63}$$

Several interesting points concerning the Runge-Kutta type method described above may be observed.

(i) The difficulty of derivatives of Y(y,t) has been successfully removed.

(ii) The error is of the same order as the Taylor's expansion.

(iii) It is only necessary to specify $t_n, \eta_n, \dot{\eta}_n$ in order to compute η_{n+1}. Thus, the specifications of an initial value problem are enough to start this method of solution for differential equations. This is in strong contrast to the numerical integration methods, $p \geq 1$, where the specifications of the initial-value problem are not enough to start the numerical solution of the problem.

(iv) The size of interval may be changed at any step since η_{n+1} is computed in terms of $t_n, \eta_n, \dot{\eta}_n$ alone, and of course h.

(v) In the case of numerical integration methods, one is interested in the solution function at $t_i = t_o + ih$, $i = 1, 2, \ldots$, and the evaluation of Y(y,t) is limited to the points t_i. In the Runge-Kutta methods, Y(y,t) is evaluated at points in addition to the points t_i. These additional evaluations of the function Y(y,t) distinguish the Runge-Kutta type method from the numerical integration methods.

(vi) The choice of the coefficients $a_1, a_2, \alpha_2, \beta_{21}$ is independent of the solution function.

(vii) The error T_R depends upon the choice of constants $a_2, a_1, \alpha_2, \beta_{21}$ and of the function y(t). The truncation error propagates as the computation is performed beyond first point t_1. The discussion of error-propagation properties of the Runge-Kutta type formulae is beyond the scope of these *Notes*. The interested reader is referred to Henrici [1] and Ralston [1] for details on the subject of errors.

(viii) The round-off errors occur due to finite precision of computation. In general, the round-off errors depend upon the type of arithmetic, fixed or floating point, and the number of bits used to specify a number in the computer. The detailed discussion of round-off errors is beyond the scope of these *Notes*. However, here again, the round-off errors are small in comparison to truncation errors in modern large-scale computers.

Example: The initial-value problem

$$\dot{y} = -y \quad , \quad y(0) = 1$$

is solved by the Runge-Kutta type method

$$\eta_{n+1} = \eta_n + h\, Y(\eta_n + \frac{h}{2}\dot{\eta}_n, t_n + \frac{h}{2})$$

where h = 0.1. The results are shown in Table VI.3.

Table VI.3

Time t	Solution by Runge-Kutta Type Method	Exact Solution
0.1	1.00000	1.00000
0.1	0.90500	0.90484
0.2	0.81902	0.81873
0.3	0.74122	0.74082
0.4	0.67080	0.67032
0.5	0.60707	0.60653
0.6	0.54940	0.54881
0.7	0.49721	0.49658
0.8	0.44997	0.44933
0.9	0.40723	0.40657
1.0	0.36854	0.36788

Exercise 7: Solve the initial-value problem

$$\dot{y} = y \quad , \quad y(0) = 1 \quad ,$$

by Runge-Kutta type methods of order 2, given by (62) and (63). Compare the results obtained by the two integration formulae.

The general case.

The Runge-Kutta type method of order m is obtained by considering the Taylor's expansion (6), and developing an expression for

$$h\,\dot{y}(t_o+nh) + \frac{h^2}{2!}\ddot{y}(t_o+nh) + \ldots + \frac{h^m}{m!}y^{(m)}(t_o+nh) \tag{64}$$

which does not involve derivatives of $Y(y,t)$, and differs from it by $O(h^{m+1})$. The suitable expression is given by

$$\sum_{i=1}^{m} a_i\, K_i \quad , \tag{65}$$

where

$$\begin{aligned} K_1 &= h\, Y(y_n, t_n) \\ K_2 &= h\, Y(y_n + \beta_{21} K_1,\ t_n + \alpha_2 h) \\ K_3 &= h\, Y(y_n + \beta_{31} K_1 + \beta_{32} K_2,\ t_n + \alpha_3 h) \\ &\quad \cdots \\ K_i &= h\, Y(y_n + \sum_{j=1}^{i-1} \beta_{ij} K_j,\ t_n + \alpha_i h) \\ &\quad \cdots \end{aligned} \tag{66}$$

The constants, a's, α's and β's, are determined as in the case of the method for m = 2. The basic steps in the procedure for the determination of these constants are outlined below.

(i) Express the total time derivatives of Y(y,t) in (64) in terms of partial derivatives. For example:

$$\ddot{y}(t_n) = [(\frac{\partial}{\partial t} + Y(y,t)\frac{\partial}{\partial y})\, Y(y,t)]\Big|_{t=t_n}$$

$$= [(\frac{\partial}{\partial t} + Y(y_n,t_n)\frac{\partial}{\partial y})\, Y(y,t)]\Big|_{t=t_n}, \qquad (67)$$

$$\dddot{y}(t_n) = [(\frac{\partial}{\partial t} + Y(y,t)\frac{\partial}{\partial y})^2\, Y(y,t)]\Big|_{t=t_n}$$

$$= [(\frac{\partial}{\partial t} + Y(y_n,t_n)\frac{\partial}{\partial y})^2\, Y(y,t)$$

$$+ Y_y(y,t)\,(\frac{\partial}{\partial t} + Y(y_n,t_n)\frac{\partial}{\partial y})\, Y(y,t)]\Big|_{t=t_n} \qquad (68)$$

and so on. (Notice, $\frac{\partial}{\partial t} + Y(y_n,t_n)\frac{\partial}{\partial y} \neq \frac{\partial}{\partial t} + Y(y,t)\frac{\partial}{\partial y}$.)

(ii) Expand Y's in (66) about the point (y_n,t_n). For example,

$$K_2 = h\, Y(y_n + \beta_{21} K_1,\ t_n\ \alpha_2 h)$$

$$= h\,\{Y(y_n,t_n) + [(\beta_{21}K_1\frac{\partial}{\partial y} + \alpha_2 h\frac{\partial}{\partial t})\, Y(y,t)]\Big|_{t=t_n}$$

$$+ [\frac{1}{2}(\beta_{21}K_1\frac{\partial}{\partial y} + \alpha_2\, h\frac{\partial}{\partial t})^2\, Y(y,t)]\Big|_{t=t_n} + \ldots\}, \qquad (69)$$

$$K_3 = h\, Y(y_n + \beta_{31}K_1 + \beta_{32}k_2,\ t_n + \alpha_3 h)$$

$$= h\,\{Y(y_n,t_n) + [((\beta_{31}K_1 + \beta_{32}K_2)\frac{\partial}{\partial y}$$

$$+ \alpha_3\, h\frac{\partial}{\partial t})\, Y(y,t)]_{t=t_n} + \frac{1}{2}[((\beta_{31}K_1 + \beta_{32}K_2)\frac{\partial}{\partial y}$$

$$+ \alpha_3\, h\frac{\partial}{\partial t})^2\, Y(y,t)]_{t=t_n} + \ldots\}, \qquad (70)$$

and so on.

(iii) Equate the coefficients of equal powers of h in the expressions for (64) and (65) so that the two expressions are equal except for $O(h^{m+1})$, for all functions $y(\cdot)$. A natural consequence of insisting that the expressions be equal for all functions $y(\cdot)$ is that

$$\alpha_i = \sum_{j=1}^{i-1} \beta_{ij} \quad , \quad i \geq 2 \ . \tag{71}$$

Further, the process of equating coefficients of equal powers of h yields the conditions that a's, α's and β's must satisfy in order that these expressions be equal except for $O(h^{m+1})$. The details of the procedure for the general case are messy and are omitted here. Ralston [1] describes the cases for m = 3 and m = 4. It is found that the fourth-order Runge-Kutta type method is suitable for most purposes. It usually happens that the constants, a's, β's, and α's, are not completely specified by these conditions. The unspecified constants are used as parameters to generate a variety of methods. These methods are all of a given order but differ in their error propagation properties. The parameters, in general, may be chosen to give desirable error propagation properties. The error properties of the Runge-Kutta type methods are presented by Henrici [1]. The comments made earlier in connection with second-order Runge-Kutta type methods hold in their entirety for the methods of higher orders.

Exercise 8: Derive the conditions on the a's, b's, α's and β's for third-order and fourth-order Runge-Kutta type methods.

The Runge-Kutta starter.

The difficulty at the start of a numerical integration method, due to the lack of the values of solution function at

$$t_o + ih \quad , \quad i = 1,\ldots,p, \quad p \geq 1 \quad ,$$

was mentioned in Section 3. In order to overcome this difficulty, advantage is taken of the fact that a Runge-Kutta type method requires only t_n, η_n, $\dot{\eta}_n$ to compute η_{n+1}. The values of the solution function at $t_o + ih$, $i = 1,\ldots,p$ are computed via a Runge-Kutta type method. At this stage, one switches to the Numerical Integration Method and the solution function is computed by the Numerical Integration Method, $n > p$.

Example: Consider the predictor-corrector method:

$$\text{Predictor:} \quad \eta_{n+1} = \eta_n + \frac{h}{2}(3\dot{\eta}_n - \dot{\eta}_{n-1})$$

$$\text{Corrector:} \quad \eta_{n+1} = \eta_n + \frac{h}{2}(\dot{\eta}_{n+1} + \dot{\eta}_n) \quad .$$

The values of the solution function at $t_o + ih$, $i = 0$ and 1 are needed to use the method. The value of the function at t_o is specified by the initial-value problem. The value of the solution function at $t_1 = t_o + h$ may be computed by a Runge-Kutta type method. In this particular example, the Runge-Kutta type method given by the difference equation

$$\eta_{n+1} = \eta_n + h\,Y(\eta_n + \frac{h}{2}\dot{\eta}_n, t_n + \frac{h}{2})$$

is used. The solution of the initial value problem

$$\dot{y} = -y \quad , \quad y(0) = 1 \quad ,$$

for $h = 0.1$, is presented again. The results are shown in

Table VI.4. The procedure of this example is the normal way of doing a problem as opposed to the earlier example on page 180.

Table VI.4

Time t				
0.0	1.00000	Initial condition		Starting Values
0.1	0.90500	Computed by Runge-Kutta type method		
	Predicted Value $\eta^{(0)}$	Corrected Value $\eta^{(1)}$	Corrected Value $\eta^{(2)}$	Exact Solution
0.2	0.81925	0.81879	0.81881	0.81873
0.3	0.74124	0.74081	0.74083	0.74082
0.4	0.67064	0.67025	0.67027	0.67032
0.5	0.60677	0.60642	0.60644	0.60653
0.6	0.54899	0.54867	0.54868	0.54881
0.7	0.49670	0.49641	0.49643	0.49658
0.8	0.44940	0.44914	0.44915	0.44933
0.9	0.40660	0.40636	0.40637	0.40657
1.0	0.36788	0.36766	0.36767	0.36788

Exercise 9: Repeat Exercise 6, where the value of the solution function at 0.1 is obtained by a Runge-Kutta starter given by (62).

5. *Comments on Numerical Solutions*

Several important topics have been omitted from the discussion of numerical methods for differential equations. It will indeed be hazardous for the reader to apply these methods without careful study of several additional topics. This comment reinforces the earlier comment that this chapter is designed to provide the basic motivation behind the techniques for the numerical solution of differential equations, rather than to enable the reader to write some of the more sophisticated programs for the solution of differential equations. A given method may be applied with confidence to a large class of problems only after a detailed study of the following properties of the method:

(i) truncation errors,
(ii) round-off errors,
(iii) bounds on propagated error,
(iv) change of interval size,
(v) stability of the numerical procedure.

These are important considerations which need to be discussed before a particular method may be used reliably and profitably.

Nordsieck's [1] method for the numerical solution of ordinary differential equations has been found by the author to be an extremely reliable method. This sophisticated method gives excellent error propagation properties. The solution may be computed at arbitrarily spaced points t_1, $t_2, \ldots, t_N$. Depending upon the nature of the solution, the routine changes the size of the interval automatically. However, this does not effect the choice of the points t_1, $t_2, \ldots, t_N$. The method was originally programmed by Nordsieck in fixed-point arithmetic for ILLIAC at The University of Illinois. More recently, the method has been programmed in Fortran IV for the Control Data Corporation 6600 computer at The University of Texas at Austin.

The numerical solutions presented in Chapter V were obtained using this method. The solution obtained by Nordsieck's method for the initial-value problem

$$\dot{y} = -y \quad , \quad y(0) = 1$$

gave excellent results. The error between the computed solution and the exact solution is less than 10^{-10} for $t_i = ih$, $i = 1,\ldots,10$, and $h = 0.1$.

APPENDIX A

O AND o SYMBOLS

The symbols O and o are used to indicate the asymptotic behavior of functions. The use of these symbols is particularly desirable in situations where the exact nature of the function is not material to the argument but its asymptotic behavior is all that is needed.

Consider the functions f(x) and g(x) defined on the set R, usually the set of reals. Let x_o be a limit point of the set R. The element x_o may or may not be in the set R.

Definitions:

(i) $$f(x) = O(g(x))$$

in R if there exists a constant α such that

$$|f(x)| \leq \alpha |g(x)|$$

for all x in R. The constant α is independent of x.

(ii) $$f(x) = O(g(x))$$

as $x \to x_o$ if there exists a neighborhood N_{x_o} of x_o such that $f(x) = O(g(x))$ in $R \cap N_{x_o}$.

(iii) $$f(x) = o(g(x))$$

as $x \to x_o$, if for every $\varepsilon > 0$, if there exists a neighborhood N_{ε,x_o} of x_o such that $|f(x)| \leq \varepsilon |g(x)|$ for x in $R \cap N_{\varepsilon,x_o}$

Examples of the use of the symbols O and o are provided by the following relationships:

$$O(f(x)) + O(f(x)) = O(f(x))$$

$$O(f(x)) + o(f(x)) = O(f(x))$$

$$o(f(x)) + o(f(x)) = o(f(x)) \quad .$$

Erdélyi [1] gives an introduction to the subject of asymptotic behavior of functions, and provides several more relationships of the form above.

APPENDIX B

MATRIX ALGEBRA

It is not the intent of this Appendix to provide a text for matrix algebra. Rather, the reader is provided, for easy reference, with two results which are important for these *Notes*. This approach has been motivated by the availability of several very good texts on the subject. For example, Bellman [2] and Gantmacher [1] discuss matrices at considerable length, and, in the present series of *Notes on System Sciences*, books of Polak and Wong [1], and Desoer [1] discuss matrix algebra in the context of linear system theory. In the latter books, the level of treatment ranges from elementary in Polak and Wong to advanced in Desoer.

1. *The Function exp(At)*

For a real or complex variable a, exp (a) may be defined by the infinite series

$$\exp(a) = 1 + \frac{a}{1!} + \frac{a^2}{2!} + \frac{a^3}{3!} + \cdots \quad . \tag{1}$$

The power series converges for all a, real or complex. Further, the convergence is uniform for every finite region of the complex plane. The function exp(A), where A is an $n\times n$ matrix, real or complex, may also be defined by the series

$$\exp(A) = I + \frac{A}{1!} + \frac{A^2}{2!} + \frac{A^3}{3!} + \cdots \quad . \tag{2}$$

Here I is the identity matrix. Exp(A), defined in this

manner, is an n×n matrix, and the series converges for all n×n matrices A, real or complex. The fact that series (2) is a convergent series follows immediately on observing:

(i)
$$\|A^n\| \leq \|A\|^n \ , \tag{3}$$

where the norm of the matrix A is defined as

$$\|A\| = \sum_{j=1}^{n} \sum_{i=1}^{n} |a_{ij}| \ ; \tag{4}$$

(ii) the series

$$\exp(\|A\|) = 1 + \frac{\|A\|}{1!} + \frac{\|A\|^2}{2!} + \ldots \tag{5}$$

is a convergent series.

In general, the evaluation of the series for exp(A) is not a simple task. Several examples, where the task is straightforward, are given below.

(i) For

$$A = \begin{bmatrix} 0 & 0 & \cdots & 0 \\ 0 & & & \\ \vdots & & & \\ 0 & \cdots & \cdots & 0 \end{bmatrix} ,$$

the zero matrix, exp(A) = I.

(ii) For

$$A = \begin{bmatrix} \lambda_1 & & & \\ & \lambda_2 & & 0 \\ & & \ddots & \\ 0 & & & \lambda_n \end{bmatrix} ,$$

a diagonal matrix,

$$\exp(A) = \begin{bmatrix} e^{\lambda_1} & & & 0 \\ & e^{\lambda_2} & & \\ & & \ddots & \\ 0 & & & e^{\lambda_n} \end{bmatrix} .$$

(iii) For

$$A = T \begin{bmatrix} \lambda_1 & & & 0 \\ & \lambda_2 & & \\ & & \ddots & \\ 0 & & & \lambda_n \end{bmatrix} T^{-1}$$

(where T is a nonsingular matrix), a diagonalizable matrix (see Section 2, below),

$$\exp(A) = T \begin{bmatrix} e^{\lambda_1} & & & 0 \\ & e^{\lambda_2} & & \\ & & \ddots & \\ 0 & & & e^{\lambda_n} \end{bmatrix} T^{-1} .$$

The usefulness of the function exp(A) arises in the solution of linear differential equations. The use of exp(A) renders the treatment of scalar and vector cases similar. The solution of the scalar differential system

$$\dot{x} = ax \quad , \quad x(0) = x_o \quad , \tag{6}$$

where x is a scalar variable and a is a scalar constant, is given by

$$x(t) = e^{at} x_o \quad .$$

Similarly, the solution to the vector differential system

$$\dot{x} = Ax \quad , \quad x(0) = x_o \quad , \tag{7}$$

where x is a vector variable and A is a constant matrix is given by

$$x(t) = e^{At}x_o \quad .$$

2. *Diagonalization of a Matrix*

Let the matrix A have n distinct eigenvalues given by $\lambda_1,\lambda_2,\ldots,\lambda_n$. Denote the corresponding eigenvectors by $h_1,h_2,\ldots,h_n$. Consider the matrix T, obtained by the adjoining eigenvectors; that is,

$$T = [h_1h_2\ldots h_n] \quad . \tag{8}$$

It may be observed that T^{-1} exists, since distinct eigenvalues lead to linearly independent eigenvectors, as shown below.

Suppose that the eigenvalues $\lambda_1,\ldots,\lambda_n$ are distinct but the eigenvectors are linearly dependent. Thus, there are constants $c_1,c_2,\ldots,c_n$, not all zero, such that

$$c_1h_1 + c_2h_2 + \ldots + c_nh_n = 0 \tag{9}$$

Let c_1 be nonzero, with no loss of generality. Consider the matrix

$$(A - \lambda_2I)(A - \lambda_3I) \ldots (A - \lambda_nI). \tag{10}$$

On multiplying both sides of (9) by the matrix (10), one obtains

$$c_1(\lambda_1 - \lambda_2)(\lambda_1 - \lambda_3) \ldots (\lambda_1 - \lambda_n) = 0 \ .$$

However,

$$\lambda_i \neq \lambda_j \quad , \quad i \neq j \quad ,$$

and this leads to $c_1 = 0$, which contradicts our hypothesis that $c_1 \neq 0$. Thus, the eigenvectors are linearly independent and T^{-1} exists.

Let $\lambda_i h_i = h_i^*$, i = 1,...,n, and

$$\Delta = \begin{bmatrix} \lambda_1 & & & 0 \\ & \lambda_2 & & \\ 0 & & \ddots & \\ & & & \lambda_n \end{bmatrix} .$$

On multiplying the matrix A with the columns of T it follows from the definition of an eigenvector that

$$A[h_1 h_2 \ldots h_n] = [h_1^* h_2^* \ldots h_n^*] \quad .$$

However, $[h_1^* h_2^* \ldots h_n^*] = T\Delta$. Thus

$$AT = T\Delta$$

or

$$A = T\Delta T^{-1} \quad .$$

This result is particularly useful in the computation of exp(A) since, from Section 1 of this Appendix,

$$\begin{aligned} \exp(A) &= \exp(T\Delta T^{-1}) \\ &= T(\exp(\Delta))T^{-1} \\ &= T \begin{bmatrix} e^{\lambda_1} & & & 0 \\ & e^{\lambda_2} & & \\ 0 & & \ddots & \\ & & & e^{\lambda_n} \end{bmatrix} T^{-1} \quad . \end{aligned}$$

The case of repeated eigenvalues is omitted here; the interested reader is referred to Desoer [1].

REFERENCES

Note: It is not uncommon to find the transliteration of Russian names appearing in several forms in the literature. In these Notes, the spelling most common in English literature is used. However, in citing references, the name is spelled as it appears in the reference. In order to facilitate the use of the bibliography, and to avoid confusion, a short table of names with alternate spellings is given below, with the most common spelling appearing first.

Andronov, Andronow
Bogoliuboff, Bogoliubov
Dorodnitsin, Dorodnicyn
Liapunov, Liapounoff, Lyapunov
Mishchenko, Miščenko
Tihonov, Tichonov
Yacubovich, Jakubovič

* * * * * * * *

Aggarwal, J. K.:

[1] "Singular Points of Planar Ordinary Differential Systems," *Journal of Differential Equations*, Vol. *3*, No. 2, 1967, pp. 203-213.

[2] "On Non-elementary Singular Points," *Journal of Franklin Institute*, Vol. *281*, No. 1, 1966, pp. 41-50.

[3] "Amplitude Bounds on Periodic and Aperiodic Oscillations: Second Order Systems," *Journal of the Inst. Math. and Its Appl.*, Vol. *3*, No. 2, 1967, pp. 202-215.

________ and Infante, E. F.:

[1] "Some Remarks on the Stability of Time-Varying Systems," *IEEE Trans. AC-13*, No. 6, 1968, pp. 722-723.

________ and Richie, C. G.:

[1] "On Coupled van der Pol Oscillators," *IEEE Trans. CT-13*, No. 4, 1966, pp. 465-466.

Aizerman, M. A., and Gantmacher, F. R.:
[1] *Absolute Stability of Regulator Systems*, Holden-Day, Inc., 1964.

Andronow, A. A., and Chaikin, C. E.:
[1] *Theory of Oscillations*, Princeton University Press, 1949.

Asner, B. A., Jr.:
[1] "Stability of a Third Order Nonlinear Differential Equation," *IEEE Trans. AC-9*, No. 4, 1964, pp. 586-587.

Baker, R. A., and Bergen, A. R.:
[1] "Lyapunov Stability and Lyapunov Functions of Infinite Dimensional Systems," *IEEE Trans. AC-14*, No. 4, 1969, pp. 325-334.

Barbashin, E. A.:
[1] "On the Stability of the Solution of a Third Order Nonlinear Equation," *Prikl. Mat. Mekh.*, Vol. *16*, 1952, pp. 629-632.

Bass, R. W.:
[1] "Mathematical Legitimacy of Equivalent Linearization by Describing Functions," *Automatic and Remote Control*, Proc. of the First International Congress of the International Federation of Automatic Control, Vol. II, Butterworths, London, 1961, pp. 895-905.

Bellman, R.:
[1] *Stability Theory of Differential Equations*, McGraw-Hill Book Co., Inc., 1953.

[2] *Introduction to Matrix Analysis*, McGraw-Hill Book Co., Inc., 1960.

Bendixson, I.:
[1] "Sur les Courbes Définies par des Équations Différentielles," *Acta Mathematica 24*, 1901, pp. 1-88.

Bergen, A. R., and Iwens, R. P., and Rault, A. J.:
[1] "On Input-Output Stability of Nonlinear Feedback Systems," *IEEE Trans. AC-11*, No. 4, 1966, pp. 742-745.

Bergen, A. R. and Sapiro, M. A.:
[1] "The Parabola Test for Absolute Stability," *IEEE Trans. AC-12*, No. 3, 1967, pp. 312-314.

Birkhoff, G., and Rota, G. C.:
[1] *Ordinary Differential Equations*, Blaisdell Publishing Company, 1969.

Bogoliubov, N. N., and Mitropolsky, Y. A.:
[1] *Asymptotic Methods in the Theory of Non-linear Oscillations*, Hindustan Publishing Corporation (India), 1961.

Brockett, R. W.:
[1] "The Status of Stability Theory for Deterministic Systems," *IEEE Trans. AC-11*, No. 3, 1966, pp. 596-606.

[2] "Variational Methods for Stability of Periodic Equations," Proc. of an International Symposium, University of Puerto Rico, *Differential Equations and Dynamical Systems*, edited by J. K. Hale and J. P. La Salle, Academic Press, 1967, pp. 299-308.

Butenin, N. V.:
[1] *Elements of the Theory of Nonlinear Oscillations*, Blaisdell Publishing Company, 1965.

Cartwright, M. L.:
[1] "van der Pol's Equation for Relaxation Oscillations," *Contributions to the Theory of Nonlinear Oscillations, Vol. II*, Princeton University Press, 1952, pp. 3-18.

________ and Littlewood, J. E.:
[1] "On Nonlinear Differential Equations of the Second Order: I. The Equation $\ddot{y} - k(1-y^2)\dot{y} + y = b\lambda k \cos(\lambda t+\alpha)$, k Large," *J. London Math. Soc.*, Vol. *20*, Part 3, No. 79, 1945, pp. 180-189.

Cesari, L.:
[1] *Asymptotic Behavior and Stability Problems in Ordinary Differential Equations*, Academic Press, Inc., 1963.

Četaev, N. G.:
[1] "Theorem Concerning the Nonstability of Regular Systems," *Prikl. Mat. Mekh.*, Vol. *8*, 1944, pp. 323-326.

Coddington, E. A., and Levinson, N.:
[1] *Theory of Ordinary Differential Equations*, Mc-

Graw-Hill Book, Co., Inc. 1955.

Courant, R.
[1] *Differential and Integral Calculus*, Vol. *1*, Interscience Publishers, Inc., 1947.

Cronin, J.:
[1] "The Point at Infinity and Periodic Solutions," *J. Diff. Eqs.*, Vol. *1*, No. 2, 1965, pp. 156-170.

de Figueiredo, R. J. P., and Chang, C.:
[1] "On the Boundedness of Solutions of Classes of Multidimensional Nonlinear Autonomous Systems," *SIAM J. Appl. Math.*, Vol. *17*, No. 4, 1969, pp. 672-680.

Desoer, C. A.:
[1] *Notes for a Second Course on Linear Systems*, Van Nostrand Reinhold Company, 1970.

________ and Shensa, M. J.:
[1] "Networks with Very Small and Very Large Parasitics: Natural Frequencies and Stability," presented in IEEE International Symposium on Circuit Theory, 1970.

Dewey, A. G.:
[1] "On the Stability of Feedback Systems with One Differentiable Nonlinear Element," *IEEE Trans. AC-11*, No. 3, 1966, pp. 485-491.

Dorodnicyn, A. A.:
[1] "Asymptotic Solution of van der Pol's Equation," *American Math. Soc., Translation, No. 88*, 1953, pp. 1-24.

Elgerd, O. I.:
[1] *Control System Theory*, McGraw-Hill Book Company, Inc., 1967.

Erdélyi, A.:
[1] *Asymptotic Expansions*, Dover Publications, Inc., 1956.

Forster, H.:
[1] "Über das Verhalten der Integralkurven einer gewöhnlichen Differentialgleichung erster Ordnung in der Umgebung eines Singulären Punktes," *Math. Zeit.*, Vol. *43*, 1937, pp. 271-320.

Gantmacher, F. R.:
[1] *The Theory of Matrices, Vol. I and Vol. II*, Chelsea Publishing Company, 1964.

Halanay, A.:
[1] *Differential Equations, Stability, Oscillations, Time Lags*, Academic Press, 1966.

Hale, J. K.:
[1] *Oscillations in Nonlinear Systems*, McGraw-Hill Book Company, Inc., 1963.

Hayashi, C.:
[1] *Nonlinear Oscillations in Physical Systems*, McGraw-Hill Book Co., Inc., 1964.

Henrici, P.:
[1] *Discrete Variable Methods in Ordinary Differential Equations*, John Wiley & Sons, Inc., 1962.

Hille, E.:
[1] *Analytic Function Theory, Vol. I*, Ginn & Company, 1959.

Hsu, J. C., and Meyer, A. U.:
[1] *Modern Control Principles and Applications*, McGraw-Hill Book Co., Inc., 1968.

Hurwitz, A.:
[1] "Ueber die Bedingungen, unter welchen eine Gleichung nur Wurzeln mit negativen reellen Theilen besitzt," *Math. Ann., Vol. 46*, 1895, pp. 273-284.

Ince, E. L.:
[1] *Ordinary Differential Equations*, Dover Publications, Inc., 1956.

Infante, E. F.:
[1] "On the Stability of Some Linear Nonautonomous Random Systems," *J. Appl. Mech.*, Vol. *35*, Series E, No. 1, 1968, pp. 7-12.

Jackson, E. K., and Aggarwal, J. K.:
[1] "Popov and Hurwitz Stability Criterions: A Comparison," *IEEE Trans. AC-11*, No. 3, 1966, pp. 623-624.

Jakubovič, V. A.:
[1] "Solution of Certain Matrix Inequalities Encountered in Nonlinear Control Theory," *Soviet Mathematics*, Vol. *5*, No. 3, 1964, pp. 652-656.

Jury, E. I., and Lee, B. W.:
[1] "On the Absolute Stability of Nonlinear Sampled-Data Systems," *IEEE Trans. AC-9*, No. 4, 1964, pp. 551-554.

________ and Ahn, S. M.:
[1] "The Theory of Inners as Applied to Networks," presented in IEEE International Symposium on Circuit Theory, 1970.

Kalman, R. E.:
[1] "Phase-Plane Analysis of Automatic Control Systems with Nonlinear Gain Elements," *Trans. of AIEE*, Vol. *73*, Part 2, Applications and Industry, 1954, pp. 383-390.

[2] "Physical and Mathematical Mechanisms of Instability in Nonlinear Automatic Control Systems," *Trans. ASME*, Vol. *79*, 1957, pp. 553-566.

[3] "Lyapunov Functions for the Problem of Lur'e in Automatic Control," *Proc. N.A.S.*, Vol. *49*, No. 2, 1963, pp. 201-205.

________ and Bertram, J. E.:
[1] "Control System Analysis and Design via the 'Second Method' of Lyapunov, I. Continuous-Time Systems," *J. of Basic Engineering*, Vol. *82*, Series D, No. 2, 1960, pp. 371-393.

Kan, E. P. F., and Jury, E. I.:
[1] "On Popov Type Criteria for ΣPFM Systems," *Internat'l J. of Control*, Vol. *13*, No. 6, 1971, pp.1121-1129.

Kaplan, W.:
[1] *Advanced Calculus*, Addison-Wesley Company, Inc., 1952.

Kokotovic, P. V., and Sannuti, P.:
[1] "Singular Perturbation Method for Reducing the Model Order in Optimal Control Design," *IEEE Trans. AC-13*, No. 4, 1968, pp. 377-384.

Krasovskii, N. N.:
[1] "On the Stability in the Large of the Solution of a System of Nonlinear Differential Equations," *Prikl. Mat. Mekh.*, Vol. *18*, 1954, 735-737.

LaSalle, J. P.:
[1] "Some Extensions of Liapunov's Second Method," *IRE Trans. CT-7*, No. 4, 1960, pp. 520-527.

________ and Lefschetz, S.:
[1] *Stability by Liapunov's Direct Method with Applications*, Academic Press, 1961.

Lefschetz, S.:
[1] *Differential Equations: Geometric Theory*, Interscience Publishers, 1963.

[2] "Notes on Differential Equations," *Contributions to the Theory of Nonlinear Oscillations*, Vol. *II*, Princeton University Press, 1952, pp. 61-73.

[3] *Stability of Nonlinear Control Systems*, Academic Press, 1965.

Levinson, N.:
[1] "A Second Order Differential Equation with Singular Solutions," *Ann. of Math.*, Vol. *50*, No. 1, 1949, pp. 127-153.

[2] "On the Existence of Periodic Solutions for Second Order Differential Equations with a Forcing Term," *J. Math. Phys.*, Vol. *XXII*, No. 2, 1943, pp. 41-48.

________ and Smith, O. K.:
[1] "A General Equation for Relaxation Oscillations," *Duke Math. J.*, Vol. *9*, No. 2, 1942, pp. 382-403.

Liapounoff, M. A.:
[1] "Probléme Général de la Stabilité du Mouvement," *Ann. Fac. Sci., Toulouse*, Vol. *9*, 1907, pp. 203-469.

Markus, L., and Yamabe, H.:
[1] "Global Stability Criteria for Differential Systems," *Osaka Math. J.*, Vol. *12*, No. 2, 1960, pp. 305-317.

Minorsky, N.
[1] *Introduction to Nonlinear Mechanics*, J. W. Edwards, 1947.

Miščenko. E. F.:

[1] "Asymptotic Calculation of Periodic Solutions of Systems of Differential Equations Containing Small Parameters in the Derivatives," *Amer. Math. Soc. Trans.*, Series 2, Vol. *18*, 1961, pp. 199-230.

Nemytskii, V. V., and Stepanov, V. V.:

[1] *Qualitative Theory of Differential Equations*, Princeton University Press, 1960.

Nordsieck, A.:

[1] "On Numerical Integration of Ordinary Differential Equations," *Mathematics of Computation*, Vol. *16*, No. 77, 1962, pp. 22-49.

Perron, O.:

[1] "Über Stabilität und Asymptotisches Verhalten der Integrale von Differentialgleichungssystemen," *Math. Zeit.*, Vol. *29*, 1929, pp. 129-160.

Pipes, L. A.:

[1] *Applied Mathematics for Engineers and Physicists*, McGraw-Hill Book Co., Inc., 1958.

Pliss, V. A.:

[1] *Nonlocal Problems of the Theory of Oscillation*, Academic Press, 1966.

Poincaré, H.:

[1] "Mémoire sur les Courbes Définies par une Équation Différentielle," *J. de Mathématiques*, *7*, 1881, pp. 375-422, and *8*, 1882, pp. 251-296.

[2] *Lecons De Mecanique Céleste*, 3 vols. 1905, 1907, 1910, Gauthier-Villars, Paris.

Polak, E., and Wong, E.:

[1] *Notes for a First Course on Linear Systems*, Van Nostrand Reinhold Company, 1970.

Pontryagin, L. S.:

[1] "Asymptotic Behavior of the Solutions of Systems of Differential Equations with a Small Parameter in the Higher Derivatives," *Amer. Math. Soc. Trans.*, Series 2, Vol. *18*, 1961, pp. 295-319.

Ponzo, P. J., and Wax, N.:

[1] "On Certain Relaxation Oscillations: Asymptotic

Solutions," *J. SIAM*, Vol. *13*, No. 3, 1965, pp. 740-766.

Popov, V. M.:
[1] "Absolute Stability of Nonlinear Systems of Automatic Control," *Automation and Remote Control*, Vol. *22*, No. 8, 1961, pp. 857-875.

Ralston, A.:
[1] *A First Course in Numerical Analysis*, McGraw-Hill Book Co., Inc., 1965.

Rapoport, A.:
[1] *Fights, Games and Debates*, The University of Michigan Press, 1960.

Rayleigh, Lord:
[1] "On Maintained Vibrations," *Phil. Mag.*, Vol. *15*, No. 94, Series 5, 1883, pp. 229-235.

Routh, E. J.:
[1] *Dynamics of a System of Rigid Bodies*, Dover Publication, Inc., 1960.

Shapovalov, V. P.:
[1] "The Integration of the System of Two Nonlinear Ordinary Differential Equations," *Vestn. Leningrad. Univ.*, *12* (1957), No. 1, pp. 188-196. (Abstract in *Mathematical Reviews*, Vol. *19*, No. 3, 1958, p. 278.)

Shensa, M. J.:
[1] "Parasitics and the Stability of Equilibrium Points of Nonlinear Networks," *IEEE Trans. on Circuit Theory*, Vol. *CT-18*, No. 4, 1971, pp. 481-484.

Struble, R. A.:
[1] *Nonlinear Differential Equations*, McGraw-Hill Book Co., Inc., 1962.

Tihonov, A. N.:
[1] "Systems of Differential Equations Containing Small Parameters in the Derivatives," *Mat. Sb. 31 (73)*, No. 3, 1952, pp. 575-586.

van der Pol, B.:
[1] "Forced Oscillations in a Circuit with Non-linear Resistance, (Reception with Reactive Triode)," *Phil. Mag.*, Vol. *3*, Series 7, No. 13, 1927, pp. 65-80.

[2] "Special Issue in Memory of Dr. Balth. van der Pol," *IRE Trans. CT-7*, No. 4, 1960.

Varaiya, P. P., and Liu, R.:
[1] "Bounded-input Bounded-output Stability for the Lur'e Problem," *IEEE Trans. AC-11*, No. 4, 1966, pp. 745-746.

Volterra, V.:
[1] *Lecons sur la Théorie Mathématique De La Lutte Pour La Vie*, Gauthier-Villars, Paris, 1931.

Wilf, H. S.:
[1] *Mathematics for the Physical Sciences*, John Wiley & Sons, Inc., 1962.

Zadeh, L. A., and Desoer, C. A.:
[1] *Linear System Theory: The State Space Approach*, McGraw-Hill Book Co., Inc., 1963.

Zames, G.:
[1] "On the Input-Output Stability of Time-varying Nonlinear Feedback Systems, Parts I & II," *IEEE Trans. AC-11*, No. 2, 1966, pp. 228-238, and *AC-11*, No. 3, 1966, pp. 465-476.

Zubov, V. I.:
[1] *Mathematical Methods for the Study of Automatic Control Systems*, Macmillan Company, 1963.

INDEX